AN EMBARRASSMENT OF PLENTY

AN EMBARRASSMENT
OF PLENTY

BY LAUREN SOTH

Thomas Y. Crowell Company
New York / Established 1834

CONTENTS

ILLUSTRATIONS

CHARTS

AN EMBARRASSMENT OF PLENTY

1 / THE FARM PROBLEM

THE HARVESTING CRISIS that struck Iowa a few years ago raised snickers from my city neighbors. The farmers did not find it so funny.

We had a severe windstorm, which blew down whole fields of corn so flat that the grain could not be harvested with corn-picking machines. The ears of corn, many broken off their stalks, had to be picked from the ground by hand, shucked free of their husks by hand, then tossed into a wagon box.

This back-breaking job was bad enough, but if it were to be accomplished efficiently, it also called for a well-trained team of horses. They could pull a wagon, stop on command, then start up again—all without the need for an extra man to do nothing but drive. A tractor or truck will not drive itself.

There are still a few pairs of old work horses on Iowa farms, kept for odd jobs and for sentimental reasons. That October they were in great demand, as farmers vied with one another to hire teams for harvesting corn.

But it turned out that many Iowa farmers did not know how to harness and hitch horses. The younger men had never hitched anything but tractors.

In few fields of human endeavor is the tempo of technological change so dramatically evident as in agriculture. The whistle-tooting steam-threshing rig that was standard for threshing oats and wheat during my own childhood is already an antique, operated today only

Picking corn by hand was a slow, arduous process that often lasted well into winter. A recent harvesting crisis in Iowa demonstrated how dependent today's farmers are on modern methods. That year a severe windstorm had blown the stalks too close to the ground for the mechanical harvesters to reach. The ears of corn had to be picked up by hand, shucked free of their husks, and thrown into horse-drawn wagons. But, in addition to the scarcity of horses, farmers were confronted with another problem—few knew how to harness and hitch the animals.

to put on nostalgic shows. Older farmers can remember tying bundles of small grain by hand, after stalks were cut by a horse-drawn reaper. Not many years before that grain was cut by a cradle scythe, and before that by a sickle.

In a century and a half the American farm has been transformed. Muscle power has been replaced by machine power of ever greater efficiency. Publicly sponsored research on a vast scale has developed better crops—animal and vegetable—and improved techniques for nurturing them. A specialized educational program without parallel in human history has disseminated this knowledge broadly. These efforts, nourished by some of the most fertile farmland in the world and encouraged by the goal of personal profit, have produced results which are a source of pride to every American.

It is hard to remember that the threat of famine clouded nearly every society in the past. Famine in the United States today is inconceivable. We have available more food, in greater variety, at lower real cost than any people have ever had anywhere. We need assign only 1 worker in every 15 to the job of producing this cornucopia (in colonial America, farming occupied 9 out of 10; in Russia today the figure is 4 out of 10), freeing manpower for the other tasks of civilized society. We are able to help other countries not only with foodstuffs but in addition with farming expertise, a significant factor in our foreign policy.

We also have the Farm Problem.

Stating the problem is simple:

1. American farmers produce more than will be consumed at today's prices, a fact dramatized by the swollen warehouses for surplus commodities that mark the landscape—including at times such unusual ones as ships on the Hudson River and caves in Kansas.
2. The federal government spends large annual sums to limit production and support farmers' prices—$4 billion in 1965.
3. And yet the income of American farmers still lags behind that of other citizens. In Iowa, one of the highest farm-income areas, in the early 1960s, farm-family income averaged $4,600 per year; the average factory worker's income was $5,200.

Understanding the problem is far from simple. Misconception has been piled upon misconception to create a badly distorted view, perhaps expressed most succinctly in the editorials of such publications as the *Wall Street Journal* and *Life*. These critics see an agriculture overrun with government bureaucrats telling the farmer what he must do. They see a ridiculous apparatus of government price-fixing, with surpluses of farm products stored at high cost and wasted. They see subsidies which are making the farmer rich at the expense of taxpayers and, worse, turning a self-reliant businessman into an unenterprising ward of the state.

This attitude may, in part, be understandable. The federal farm programs *do* seem absurd. They often are inconsistent, conflicting, and contradictory. They are outrageous when viewed in the context of the *laissez-faire* philosophy of government's place in the economy. They are never neat, logical, elegant; but, rather, clumsy, loose, ambiguous, a crazy-quilt of expediency.

Even the economic thinkers who are accepting a bigger role for government in the economy often shudder after a quick look at the

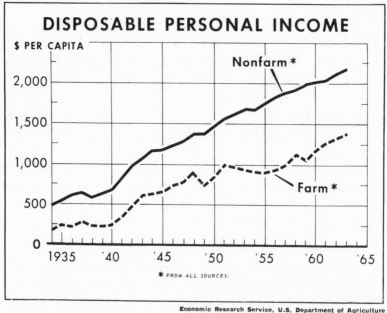

Economic Research Service, U.S. Department of Agriculture

In spite of efforts to boost farm prices, American farm incomes continue to lag behind those of other workers. The disposable personal incomes of the last thirty years show how the gap has widened.

[4]

Dramatic changes have transformed American farming over the last few generations. The combine, above, harvests today's crops in a single operation. Only a generation ago farmers had to cut the grain and then take it to a stationary thresher, operated by steam. Older farmers remember tying the bundles by hand after horse-drawn reapers had cut the stalks. And not many years before that the grain was cut by a cradle scythe.

farm programs. The one comment that is general after a discussion of the national economy and the federal budget is that farm subsidies should be reduced. The usual picture is one of government regimentation and failure.

[5]

This pessimistic picture is not true.

Most of the so-called controls are voluntary. The farmer is free to accept government regulations on crop acreage in return for the rewards from so doing. Or he can stay out.

Federal regulation is not expanding, as is often implied. For all practical purposes, the government acreage-control programs are the same as they were in the early 1930s.

Even with these allegedly onerous controls around his neck, the American farmer still is less subject to rules and regulations, public and private, than any other production worker in modern society. Certainly he is not the self-sufficient yeoman his grandfather was. He is dependent on the world outside his fence lines, including government, but he has lost far less of the freedom of an earlier society than the rest of us. Compare him to the three-fourths of us earning a living as employees, subject to orders of our employers, our labor unions, and our government. The farmer still works when and as much as he pleases. He runs his farm as he pleases.

The continuing freedom of the farmer is one reason, in fact, that the control programs seem so unworkable and generally get such a bad press. The programs were developed to maintain that freedom while still retarding overproduction and protecting farm income. Serving such diverse purposes makes them appear illogical, and they do not appeal to those who strive for ideological purity—either the worshipers of the "free" market or the advocates of strict government management.

This also makes them expensive. Considering all the benefits, however, the cost in recent years is not exorbitant. Studies by research economists in the U.S. Department of Agriculture, at Iowa State University, Cornell University, Pennsylvania State University, and Oklahoma State University indicate that crop-acreage control, price support, and commodity-storage programs increased net farm income by about $6 billion per year, or 80 to 100 per cent in the early 1960s. The cost to the government was approximately $3 billion per year.

These policies have achieved two major objectives: They have kept the farmer reasonably independent, and they have guaranteed an abundance of farm produce. They have not completely achieved two other objectives: They have not prevented wasteful surpluses, nor have they adequately compensated the farmer for his effort and investment. In addition, they have required the expenditure of substantial sums of tax funds—to some critics their worst failure.

This is the problem of agriculture in an affluent America. It does not result from the sinister plotting of farmers, processors, or distributors. Neither can it be blamed on political bumbling. The causes lie deep in American history.

2 / THE AMERICAN FARMER TODAY

TODAY A FARMER must be more a mechanic than a weather prophet, more a scientist than a good judge of growing things.

To be sure, modern agriculture is not all science. It is also an art, as of old. The skills of judging when to cultivate corn or what is the best combination of grasses for a certain pasture seeding cannot all be learned from books. But for a long time the trend in the United States has been sharply toward more application of science.

The modern farmer knows more industrial-type skills than half the people working in cities. He knows more about gasoline engines, building construction, electricity, wiring, and pumps than most city people.

Living conditions have become more like those of the city, also. The farmer and his family usually live in a house which is about the same as the house of his brother's family in the city—except that it probably is larger. Practically all farm homes in the United States to-day (98 per cent of them) have central station electric service. Running-water systems and flush toilets are not as widespread as in towns and cities (about one-fourth of farm homes lack them), but these conveniences are commonplace and increasing in all farming areas, and soon will be "standard equipment" nearly everywhere.

When one talks about farming or farmers in the vast continental sweep of the United States, he must define what *area* and what *kind* of farming he is talking about. American agriculture ranges from tropical to north-temperate zone crops, from humid to arid; almost every kind of agriculture may be found in the 50 states. I will talk mostly about agriculture in Iowa, in the central corn belt of the country, because I know it best and because it is most typical of the nation as a whole. This is general farming, with a wide variety of crops and livestock. The main crop is corn, and this grain provides the basis for the great livestock industries of the central plains—hogs, beef cattle, dairying, sheep, poultry.

The farms in this region are individual family-type farms; that is, most of them are operated by individual farmers. The farmer and his family provide nearly all the labor and the management for the business.

The family lives on the land. In most of Europe and the rest of the world outside of North America, farmers usually live in villages, with all the farmhouses clustered together. Farmers go from the villages to the surrounding land each day to conduct their farming operations. But in the United States and Canada, a different pattern developed. Here the farmhouses dot the countryside. Now that farms are becoming so much larger, with improved machinery and greater labor efficiency, the distances between the dwellings are lengthening.

Let us visit a typical grain and livestock farm in central Iowa. This farm is a good model for all the vast area from Pennsylvania and New York westward to central Nebraska and Kansas, and from Kentucky-Missouri-Kansas north to the Canadian border. In fact you would find some farms like this one all over the United States, but it is the most common variety in the central region.

This farm contains 260 acres, or a little more than 100 hectares of land. About 20 acres are in woods, with a creek running through. Another 40 acres are in permanent pasture on hillsides. The pastureland could be plowed and cultivated, but it slopes steeply, making erosion difficult to control. Since the farmer maintains a herd of 30 to 40 Hereford beef cows and raises calves, he prefers to keep these hills in permanent grass.

The "farmstead"—the house and other buildings and a cattle feedlot—take up about five acres. The house is a two-story, wooden house painted white. It was built by the present owner's father in 1924. In recent years, the house has been slightly remodeled and modernized. A few years ago the Carl Johnsons (as I shall call the family) put in new kitchen equipment, including electric stove, washing machine, clothes dryer, refrigerator, and electric dishwasher. An old cream-separator room, remnant of the days when the Johnsons had a dairy business, was torn off the side of the house. In its place, a new bathroom with shower, for the men to clean up in after work in the fields, replaces the old milkroom. Otherwise, this 40-year-old house is about the same as when it was built.

Like many other farmers, Mr. Johnson has become more specialized in his business of late years. I mentioned that he dropped his dairy herd. Also the Johnsons no longer keep chickens. Mrs. Johnson was very glad to see the old chickenhouse removed and to escape from the drudgery of taking care of chickens and marketing the eggs. Nowadays the Johnsons buy milk and eggs for their table in the grocery store in town.

The time and effort that were used in dairying and poultry raising now are spent on the beef cattle herd and the large hog-raising enterprise. Mr. Johnson plans to market 40 to 60 steers and heifers each year, mostly animals he has raised himself, although he buys some thin cattle occasionally to place in his feedlot for fattening.

He also raises about 500 head of hogs each year. He ordinarily has 50 to 60 sows farrowing during the year. He will have some sows farrowing pigs every other month most years.

Mr. Johnson raises nearly all the feed for his hogs and cattle himself. He seldom sells any corn. Of his 195 acres of cropland, he usually has 115 acres of corn. The other 80 acres, not always the same acres, are sometimes in soybeans, in oats, and in legume crops—mostly alfalfa for hay.

This is a large business; in recent years the annual gross sales have ranged from $30,000 to $40,000. Cost of production has been about $25,000 a year, leaving a net income of $5,000 to $15,000. The average net income for the last 10 years has been about $8,000 per year. Does the net income seem small for such a large total of sales? Fertilizer, machinery, insecticides, weed-killer, gasoline, feed supplement, animal medicine, and other costs are heavy.

The Johnsons have four children, two boys 18 and 16, and two girls 21 and 12. The older girl just finished college and is soon to be married. The older boy is enrolled in Iowa State University for a course in mechanical engineering. The younger boy is in his last year of high school. He has not yet made up his mind whether he wants to go into farming or to seek another career like his brother. The younger daughter is in the eighth grade.

Like many other farm families, the Johnsons would be happy to see their children stay in farming. But they are realistic and recognize that opportunities for good incomes in farming are limited. They realize that a young person beginning farming finds it very difficult these days to get the capital to start a new farm business for himself. Mr. Johnson has told the younger boy that he will help him get started on his own, or take him into partnership on the old home farm, if he wants to become a farmer. But he does not put pressure on the boy, preferring to let him make up his own mind.

The Johnsons own two automobiles, and both cars are kept busy on trips to the nearby town of Waukee or to the city of Des Moines only 12 miles away.

Farming today is far from the isolated, self-sufficient occupation it was 50 years ago or even 30 years ago. The Johnsons spend much time visiting friends or going to baseball, basketball, and football games, the movies, or shopping in Des Moines.

If you saw the Johnson family walking down Locust Street in Des Moines, you would not be able to tell whether they were a farm family or a Des Moines lawyer's family. The girls and their mother are dressed in the latest fashion. Their hairdos are the product of a beauty parlor, the same as those of their city sisters.

The Johnsons receive a daily morning newspaper, the *Des Moines Register,* delivered to their mailbox. They also subscribe to the local weekly newspaper, a state farm paper, a national farm magazine, two monthly women's magazines, and a national news magazine. In addition, members of the family often pick up other magazines on newsstands. The family has a fairly large collection of books, larger than most families have, either city or farm. Mrs. Johnson is the daughter of a college professor and was a teacher in high school before she married. She is a lover of literature and has succeeded in indoctrinating her children in the beauty and the worth of good books. When they were younger she read every evening to the children.

Like nearly every other American family, the Johnsons have a television set and several radios, including one in one of the automobiles. Mr. Johnson does not have a radio on the tractor he uses for field work, as many farmers do, although the boys have been urging him to get one so that they could listen to the baseball games while cultivating corn or cutting hay.

Mr. Johnson had a "full line" of farm equipment at one time—including a combine, corn sheller, corn picker, plows, harrows, hay baler, ensilage cutter, and many other items. However, in the last few years he has found that it pays him to hire some work done by a neighbor—or to trade certain kinds of machine work with neighbors. For example, he no longer has a combine and uses a neighbor's. In return, he allows his neighbor to use his corn sheller.

The latest bit of machinery to be brought into the Johnson enterprise is a new automatic feeder for the beef cattle. This is a large auger run by electric motors, taking the mixed feed (corn, protein supplement, and minerals) directly from the storage bin to the feed troughs, eliminating a lot of backbreaking shovel work.

I have gone into considerable detail in describing the Johnson farm and the Johnson farm family because both are illustrative of a wide segment of American farming. But it should be clear that the Johnsons are members of the very top echelon of American farming—the upper 10 per cent in income. (See table, p. 14.) They are among the established commercial farm families who are able to maintain a high-level urban standard of living.

To illustrate another and larger part of American farming, let me tell about another family in our neighborhood near Des Moines. Call them the John Kellys. John Kelly is about 45. He inherited a fairly good farm of 160 acres, the one on which he was born and has lived all his life. He finished high school and took one year of a short course in agriculture at Iowa State University. He is a hard worker and intelligent, but he has not been able to get ahead as a farm operator.

His cash income probably has averaged below $3,000 a year in the last five years. He has been unable to afford repairs on the old farm home. While his mother and father were alive, for nearly 20 years, John and his wife and children lived in a second house on the farm, a small, three-room cottage without a bathroom. Now they have moved

Proportions of farms and product sales in different classes of farms, with average family incomes of operators, 1959

SALES PER FARM	PROPORTION OF—[a]		AVERAGE FAMILY INCOME [b]		
	NUMBER OF FARMS	SALES OF PRODUCTS	FROM FARMING [c]	OFF-FARM	TOTAL
	PER CENT	PER CENT			
$40,000 or more	2.8	31.5			
$20,000–$39,999	5.7	18.5			
$10,000–$19,999	13.0	21.9			
$10,000 or more	21.5	71.9	$7,982	$1,978	$9,960
$1,000–$9,999	17.6	15.4	3,451	1,567	5,018
Less than $5,000:					
Mainly farming [d]	26.1	8.9	1,938	1,517	3,455
Part-time and part-retirement	34.8	3.8	579	3,521	4,100
All farms	100.0	100.0			

[a] From the 1959 Census of Agriculture.

[b] From *Food and Agriculture, a Program for the 1960's,* USDA, March 1962, p. 50.

[c] Includes nonmoney income from food and housing.

[d] Farms with sales of $2,500 to $4,999, plus farms with sales of $50 to $2,499 whose operators were less than 65 years old and who either worked off farm fewer than 100 days, or, with other family members, had nonfarm income less than farm sales.

into the big house, but it still is far short of convenience and comfort. The Kellys have three girls and a boy, all bright, personable youngsters. Because they live on a farm and the family income is low, they probably will be unable to get the education their intelligence justifies. At least it will be much more difficult for them than for children of a skilled factory worker in Des Moines.

Kelly lacks managerial capacity, apparently, and in today's agriculture there is not much room for a farm operator who is hard-working but incapable of management. Since he has only 160 acres of land of his own, with only 100 crop acres, Kelly farmed a few small fields on shares with nonfarming owners. He planted and harvested corn for me on my small acreage for several years. He is always up-to-date in his knowledge of new methods. He attends extension meetings and is an enthusiastic participant in activities of the soil-conservation district in our county.

One day I told another neighbor, a successful operator of a large corn and livestock farm, that John Kelly was such a good farmer I couldn't understand why his income was so low. A few weeks later I learned that the big operator had hired Kelly to work for him. Kelly is probably making more money than he did before, and his managerial responsibilities are less. He still operates the home place, but he spends a lot of his time working on the big farm. The big farmer's machinery is available to him for some of his own crop work. He has discontinued his small hog enterprise.

This is a kind of adjustment which many farmers may find advisable in the future. The Kellys prefer to live in the country or they long ago could have moved to more lucrative employment in the city. Now they have the advantage of regular paychecks, with some security, along with life on the farm and an extra business of their own, crop raising. Kelly did not have enough of a business on the home place to occupy his full time, and he apparently did not know how to expand it through more livestock production. Now, under the guidance of an able farm manager, he can be more productive.

You can find almost every kind of farm organization in America—

everything from giant corporation farms to small vegetable farms of 10 acres or less. In California, Texas, Arizona, and the states around the Gulf of Mexico, there are many big fruit and vegetable farms, employing large numbers of hired laborers. In the Great Plains states from Texas up to Montana there is a sprinkling of giant wheat farms which are not of the individual family-type, because they employ many hired workers. Also, some cattle and sheep ranches in the western states are of this type.

An interesting change in farm living has been taking place in some of the wheat and cattle country of the western states. This is a trend

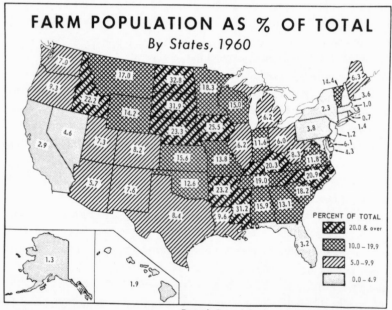

Economic Research Service, U.S. Department of Agriculture

The importance of farming to some states is indicated by the concentration of farm families in certain areas of the country. The percentage of population living on the farm ranges from 0.7 percent in Rhode Island to 32.8 percent in North Dakota.

[16]

back to the European style of farmers living in villages and not out on the land itself. The modern methods of producing wheat permit a specialized wheat grower to live in town and to travel out to his farm for plowing, seeding, spraying, and harvesting. Also, many cattle ranchers can live in town and still manage their cattle-raising enterprises. All of America has become so mobile as a result of the automobile and good roads that a farmer is not tied to his land in the same way his father and grandfather were. Even in Iowa a few farm families live in town, rather than out on the land. However, the trend to this kind of living has not gone very far except in the wheat and cattle country.

Foreign visitors to Iowa often tell me that the mode of living of farm families is quite different from what they expected. They expect to find modern refrigerators, central-heating systems, modern plumbing, electrical equipment, and so on. But they find it remarkable that farm people in this country take up the same kinds of recreation and entertainment that city folks do. The typically "rural" games and pastimes are gradually disappearing.

For example, several farmer friends of mine even play golf. A few years ago this was unheard of. Today farmers not only have more leisure time, some of them actually enjoy the exercise of golf. They do not perform as much physical labor as in the old days. Farm families have taken up the sport of swimming increasingly in recent years. A few wealthier farmers have built concrete swimming pools on their farms. Others use ponds built mainly for conservation purposes for family swimming and fishing.

Enough Iowa farmers take vacations in Florida, Arizona, and California during the winter months to attract attention. All the year round they drive their cars to cities such as Des Moines, Omaha, Davenport, Kansas City, St. Louis, Chicago, and Minneapolis. They go to the theater, sporting events, art museums, music halls, and other cultural and recreational centers.

The farm family no longer lives in semi-isolation, as it did just a few years ago. One major reason for this has been the rise of modern farm technology. A farmer no longer can carry on his business as an independent operator. He is dependent on the automobile repair shop, the farm machinery spare parts business, the oil and gasoline business, the veterinarian, the fertilizer salesman, and a host of others. Half a century ago a farmer could carry on virtually alone, if he had to, spending very little cash and never showing himself in town. His power came from horses, raised on the farm and "fueled" with oats and hay grown on the farm. He used no commercial fertilizer. He had no machinery he could not repair himself, because he usually had a forge and could do rudimentary blacksmithing without help.

Today an Iowa farmer hardly can operate his farm for one week without calling on nonfarm business for supplies or services. The modern farm is so integrated into the nonfarm economy that it is no wonder farm-family living has become integrated into the urban society.

In Iowa we have had many visits of delegations from the Soviet Union. Former Premier Nikita Khrushchev was fascinated with the production techniques of Iowa agriculture, especially modern methods of corn raising and livestock feeding. So the Soviet government sends many groups of Russian farm experts to Iowa. These delegations find it astonishing that farming is so "industrialized," in using machinery, mechanical power, and chemicals, but still retains the independent family farm as the basic business organization in agriculture. According to Marxist theory and experience in many other countries besides Russia, modern agriculture should lead to large-scale farms on the collective or corporate pattern. American agriculture does not fit this pattern, which is an inexplicable "contradiction" to the Russians.

But it is not surprising at all. The individual family-business enterprise just happens to be the most efficient for American conditions. We shall discuss this in more detail in a later chapter. There are no legal or other restrictions against any kind of farm organization—corporation, cooperative, partnership; there are no restrictions as to size. Industrialization of agriculture has not brought factory-style agriculture to America—and shows no signs of doing so—simply because individual enterprise is more efficient.

The incentives for introducing new methods and improving effi-

U.S. Department of Agriculture

Before the mechanical revolution, farmers used primitive methods to clear and cultivate the soil. Rather than specializing in one crop to sell at the market, they raised practically everything they needed to feed and clothe their families. Above, a frontier farm, about 1880.

ciency appear to be much more effective in individual family-enterprise farming than in collective farming. One needs to observe American farmers only a very short time before he realizes how this incentive system works. A new crop variety, a new type of fertilizer, a new farm machine, a new technique—these are put into practice very rapidly. A farmer is compelled by the force of competition to "keep up" if he is to maintain his income position. Bankers, cooperatives, and federal agencies readily lend money for such cost-reducing capital investments.

Modern farming, with its dependence on the nonfarm economy, has lost some elements of freedom. The farmer is not entirely free to do as he pleases if he wants to stay in business. But in return for this

[19]

loss of freedom, the farmer has gained in income, leisure, and better living.

The farmer also has lost a degree of freedom through government programs which exert pressure on him to control acreage of certain crops, regulate market prices, provide subsidies for soil conservation, and so on.

However, the loss of freedom from both of these outside forces is very slight. There is nothing to prevent the farmer from ignoring the government programs and ignoring modern technology—if he chooses to live in the style of 100 years ago. A few farm families living in the mountainous areas of the southern states or in the cutover timberlands of the lake region or in the mountain valleys of the west actually do live this way. But for the great bulk of American farm families, modern farm technology and modern government regulations are welcome in return for the economic advantages they yield.

American agriculture's great success in adapting science and improving productivity must be credited, in large degree, to the system of free enterprise which encourages private investment and risk-taking.

The Soviet Union, in contrast, cannot seem to draw the investment into agriculture that is needed for modern technology. The state, which controls investment, cannot spare the resources from heavy industry, armament production, and other claims that take priority over farming; although this has been changing somewhat under Khrushchev and his successors.

United States private investment in agriculture is so much more flexible and responsive to new opportunities that this in large measure explains America's superior agricultural performance. However, this is not the only reason, as we shall see in later chapters. American agricultural success did not just happen by accident. It was planned.

3 / THE FAMILY FARM

THE UNITED STATES is a country of independent family farms. That calls for a definition. There can be ·many different concepts of a "family farm." In this book we are thinking of a farm operated as a business enterprise, in which most of the labor and most of the management are performed by the same family. In nonfarm business, such firms might be called the family shop, the family store, the family bakery, the family brickyard. The family farm is the same kind of enterprise in agriculture.

This has nothing to do with land ownership. A family farm may be wholly a tenant farm or partly owned and partly rented, providing the farmer has managerial control and he and his family supply most of the labor.

The family farm, preferably the family-*owned* farm, always has been the ideal in the United States. American political theory, ideals, and objectives of democracy shaped the system of farm land-tenure and the policy of farm organization.

Early American statesmen, particularly Thomas Jefferson, believed that the strongest foundation for democracy was the free, independent farmer owning and operating his farm. The small-scale farmer of the colonial period developed the independent attitude of mind which has been characteristic of the American people ever since.

The words "free" and "equal" expressed the dominant ideas of the young United States. There was a strong belief that individual personal freedom could not be maintained under a system of large land-holdings and feudal estates operated by hired labor.

At the time of the Revolution there were enormous holdings of land throughout the 13 colonies. In the middle states were the large estates of the New York Dutch patroons and the stately manors of Pennsylvania and Maryland. In the south, of course, were the extensive plantations of the sugar, rice, cotton, and tobacco planters.

But even in the south as well as throughout the colonies, small, independent farmers predominated. When the colonies were settled, mostly by Englishmen, huge land grants were made to friends of the king. These manorial holdings largely gave way to smaller farms over the years.

In New England a system of dividing land among settlers by lot was worked out in democratic fashion. Each family received some of the better as well as some of the poorer land. The uncultivated land was used as a common pasture, and herdsmen were hired by the community to handle all the livestock together. This New England system provided security of title to the landowner and it established an orderly way of dividing up the land.

In Virginia new settlers were granted 50 acres of unoccupied land as "head rights." Sea captains and merchants acquired head rights which they sold to immigrants. Those who traveled back and forth across the Atlantic often received head rights each time they landed in the southern colonies, and often they secured head rights for servants or for sailors who never planned to settle.

In this and various other ways land was divided up from the original large land grants. In the modern world we would call this "land reform," since it resulted in the land being occupied and farmed by individual families. Many large estates remained along with the small farms. But even in colonial days there were good opportunities for the small, independent farmer.

The American colonists had left the old countries of Europe, partly to flee from the feudal land systems there. The feudal land system they knew was the backbone of the monarchial political system. Political

U.S. Department of Agriculture

The problem of too much. The efficiency of modern farming has led to our number one farm problem—overproduction. With many major crops, farmers face a market already swollen with a surplus of goods, as illustrated by the 40,000 bales of cotton, above. The federal government spends about $4 billion every year to limit production and support prices.

organization from the king down to the lowest serf was based upon unequal rights and subjugation. There was a pyramid of superior-inferior tenure relationships on the land. Every person, except the king, held his land under someone else and was subservient to the people above him in the hierarchy.

[23]

The American colonists placed great importance on equality, with every man on an even basis with his neighbor. In the Declaration of Independence, Americans held it to be a "self-evident truth" that men were created "free and equal." This concept was the firm foundation for the family-farm policy.

The family-farm theme pervades all American agricultural legislation and action. No other single idea has had such a profound effect on American agriculture.

Even today much of the effort of the federal government in agriculture is designed to favor family farms as defined here. The Farmers Home Administration, originally the Farm Security Administration, was established for the purpose of providing easy loans and technical and managerial help for families who want to own their own farms. Nearly all farm legislation states as its objective the promotion of the well-being of family-farm operators.

The development policy of the United States was fairly well established even before the federal Constitution was ratified. The land ordinances passed by the Continental Congress confirmed formally the understood purpose of developing the public lands. Later the federal union Congress carried on this policy. The land ordinance of 1785 provided that the new lands of the western territory would be sold at auction at a minimum price of $1 per acre. One section of each township was to be reserved for the maintenance of public schools. In the ordinance of 1787, Congress provided that the Northwest Territory eventually would become at least three but not more than five territories. When a territory numbered 60,000 inhabitants it might frame a constitution and apply for admission into the Union on equal terms with the original 13 states. There were to be no new "colonials" without political privileges in the new country. The ordinance also guaranteed certain basic individual freedoms and prohibited slavery in the new territory.

For a half-century after the land ordinances, a vigorous debate was carried on about opening up the new lands. The principal issues were whether land should be sold in small parcels to settlers, or perhaps given away, or sold to individuals or companies in large areas for resale. A series of land laws was passed, culminating in the Homestead Act of 1862. This provided free land in 160-acre parcels for those who would live on the land and develop it.

As early as 1800 the political pressure of frontier farmers began to show its influence. The pressure was for lower prices of the public land and the sale of smaller acreages.

Eastern landowners and manufacturers opposed liberalizing the public-land policy. They saw the value of their real estate undermined by the opening up of the newer lands in the west. They also thought western land opportunities would compete for their labor supply and force higher wages. They rationalized their self-interest in a conservative land policy by expounding the view that if the government gave away land it would encourage laziness and the settlers would become paupers.

The frontier farmers and land developers, however, won out decisively. By 1820 it was possible to buy public land in parcels as small as 40 acres, and the minimum price, which had been raised to $2 an acre in 1796, was lowered to $1.25. The minimum price tended to become the maximum price because of an abundance of land and the united public opinion of the new settlers.

There was a great deal of land speculation and crooked dealings in the opening up of the western lands. Vast acreages of the best timber and mining lands passed into the hands of large corporations, even after the Homestead Act. Dummy homesteaders and employees were used to defeat the purposes of the legislation. Nevertheless, land was largely made available at very low cost or free to prospective farmers. In all the period from the Revolution to the end of the nineteenth century, in fact, anyone who wanted to farm in the United States could get a farm virtually free of monetary cost.

Of course, he had to be willing to undergo the hardship of developing new land. But there were huge areas of cultivable land, and after the Louisiana Purchase of 1803 opened up the entire Missouri River basin, much of it was without even forests, just waiting for the plow.

Probably no policy of the young United States did so much to implant the doctrine of social equality as the land-development policy. In all the western territories there was almost complete social equality. People who moved from the eastern cities or immigrants who came from abroad to settle on family-sized farms of the middle west would not tolerate stratification of their communities.

Slavery continued in the south until the Civil War and a master-servant relationship long after. Indeed, the United States still falls short of its ideals of social equality, not only in the south but throughout the country. Progress continues, and Americans are approaching more closely to their ideal as time goes on. Much remains to be done and perhaps the ideal of perfect equality of opportunity will never be reached, human nature being what it is.

But the point to be made here is the overriding importance of a policy of equal land distribution and of family-farm organization to the establishment of social equality. It was the family farmers of the northern and western states who fought the evil of slavery until it was finally abolished. Their philosophy that every man is as good as his neighbor has penetrated the entire American social fabric. It was this philosophy which made America so inviting to the millions of immigrants who fled their homelands to seek new opportunity in a new world.

In the new farming communities of growing nineteenth-century America, the banker, the storekeeper, the schoolteacher, the blacksmith, and the carpenter were all farmers in spirit and thinking. More than likely, each of them had been raised as a farmer's boy and took up a new occupation as the needs of the community arose.

The "hired men" on the farms usually were sons of neighboring farmers or of townspeople. They lived in the house with the same rights as all the rest of the family. The hired man ate his meals with the family, sat in the parlor with the family when neighbors came

The family farm, which still predominates in America, is partially an outgrowth of the frontier. As the country expanded westward, land was readily available to those who would risk the hardships of developing it. Above, a sod farmhouse in the Oklahoma Territory.

"a-visiting," and knelt for evening prayers with the family. Often he married the boss's daughter and later established his own farm.

Although the technology of farming and the economic growth of the nation have greatly changed the patterns of farm and small-town life, the pioneer principle of social equality prevails to a large degree throughout America. It is the source of the drive for equality of opportunity which, as we have said, is still going on.

It is interesting to speculate what the course of United States history might have been had the landholding patterns of Europe been

[27]

transplanted in America. Suppose that large farming estates, with tenant-farm families subject to the mercies of an all-powerful landlord, had prevailed in the development of the western lands. Suppose, instead of handing out the land in equal shares to farmers who would cultivate it, the government had sold the land to the highest bidders.

If those had been the policies, slavery probably would not have been confined to a few southern states and then eliminated.

It is doubtful that America would have developed its renowned system of free public education under a different land policy. Almost the first building to go up in a new farming community in pioneer days after the homes were built was the community school. The American pioneers had a profound faith in education and they insisted that schools be opened to all. The democratic ideals of the people caused them to insist on establishing public schools. They protested against the aristocratic practices and purposes of most of the private schools of the early nineteenth century.

It would be stretching the historical evidence too far to claim that the enlightened farmland policy of the United States was the *sole* force behind the movement for public schools, equal voting rights, the elimination of slavery, and the guarantees in law and custom of social equality. But that the land policy had a strong influence on all these cannot be doubted.

Michael Soth, born in 1816 in Kork near Baden-Baden, Germany, and by trade a blacksmith, came to America in 1836 to make his way in the New World. He couldn't speak English, of course, being a poor, uneducated member of the working class of Baden. But when he landed in New York he showed the proprietor of a smithy that he knew how to make horseshoe nails and got a job. How long he stayed in New York building up a financial reserve is uncertain. Apparently not many months before he worked his way west to Butlerville and Pleasant Plain, Ohio. For by 1843 he was well enough established in Butlerville as a farmer and still part-time blacksmith to get married.

His wife, a native-born American of German stock, presented

Michael with seven sons and five daughters. One son died in infancy, but the other six fought on the Union side in the Civil War. Michael Soth had prospered so well that he was able to give each of his six sons a farm of about 160 acres at the end of the war. (He undoubtedly also helped other members of his family to emigrate to America. Ultimately, his two brothers, one of his two sisters, and his widowed mother came to live in the United States.) One of the sons, William Penn, who was born in 1847 and fought in the war as a teenager, elected to take his farm in Iowa. He was my grandfather.

William Penn Soth settled in Tama County, Iowa, about 1866 and started farming. In 1873 he married Mary Matilda Tompkins, who was born in Girard, Michigan, in 1849 and came to Iowa in a covered wagon with her parents in 1853. Abram Tompkins, her father, bought a large amount of Tama County land, but he and some of his fellow pioneers from the east wanted neighbors and were so bighearted (as family legend would have it) that they sold some of their land to newcomers at the bargain price they had paid, $1.25 an acre.

My grandmother, Mary Matilda, loved to tell her grandchildren stories about her childhood and of her schooling in a log schoolhouse. She later went to the Irving Academy at Irving, Iowa, a town now extinct, and then taught school for two years before her marriage. One of her yarns seems so fantastic that readers of this book probably will not believe it; they will regard it as an innocent piece of grandmotherly fiction or a case of her listener's childlike gullibility. But I'll tell it, anyway, because it dramatizes the privation of the times and the frontier spirit of sharing.

Grandmother said that when she was teaching school, or perhaps it was when she was going to school herself as a child, one family, newcomers to the area, was so poor that at first it couldn't provide shoes for the children to wear to school. In the winter the children heated hardwood boards in the fireplace before starting to school. Then, carrying the hot boards under their arms, they'd run through the snow barefoot until their feet were nearly frozen, stand on the boards while catching their breath, dash on for another hundred yards or so, warm up on the boards, and so on to another cabin and finally to school. The neighbors, however, soon supplied some shoes.

I wish I could report that the shoeless children went on to finish school, become successful farmers, lawyers, and doctors. But Grandmother did not relate the sequel. Even when I first heard it as a boy of 10 or so, I was truly impressed that any kid would run to school in winter barefoot. I couldn't imagine such a desire for education.

Grandmother's story is a vignette of pioneer life and the passionate urge to make new homes on the land. It also tells of the companion urge for education. Both were important in the building of American agricultural policy.

There is nothing whatsoever unusual about this family history. (On my mother's side, the background is similar, except for an earlier beginning in Pennsylvania and a large number of preacher-farmers in each generation.) I tell it in capsule form here because it is so typical of the development of the farming areas of the middle west. Abram Tompkins was not unusually benevolent. He reflected the democratic, egalitarian spirit of the frontier when he sold back some of his land at the purchase price to newcomers. I suspect that community pressure against excessive landholdings had something to do with his behavior. The people developing the new lands thought the wealth should be evenly divided, at least in the early stages, and they strongly resented the eastern land companies which brought up large tracts.

The frontier attitude had won legal expression in laws passed by Congress which sanctioned the prior rights of the families living on the land to its purchase. Before much of the land in the middle west was surveyed, pioneers had moved onto it. When it was put up for sale, these "squatters" banded together in groups to put forward their claims, and selected a bidder to speak for them at the land auctions. After passing special laws legalizing the action of particular groups, Congress finally in 1841 passed the Pre-emption Act and in 1854 the Graduation Act. These laws gave the heads of families the right to settle on 160 acres of unsurveyed public land and the right to purchase it at the minimum price when the land was placed on sale. Ultimately, the spirit of the frontier on landholdings led to the Homestead Act.

This was only three or four generations ago. Present-day Americans should not find it hard to understand the hunger for equal land distribution in the "new" countries of today—those that are breaking away from their feudal past and demanding the breakup of the haciendas in Latin America, for example. If there is violence and extralegal squatting on public, church, and private estate land, this mirrors America's own past. The difference is only that Americans had so much more land available. It was new land, and the developers of it insisted on an equal start for everyone. They had their land "reform" at the beginning, which made it a lot easier than the land-reform movements of today. But there was a measure of violence, and our great-grandfathers occasionally did take the law into their own hands.

4 / FOOD AND
ECONOMIC PROGRESS

Food is such a routine part of our lives that we find it difficult to regard it as an important factor in social and economic development. It's like the air we breathe or the water we drink: it's there, we eat it; it's always been there and always will be.

But food is not just "there." It must be produced, transported, processed, cooked—all of which require human effort, organization, skill, and knowledge.

Food is important to any human activity. The kind and amount of work men are able to do depend on the food they eat. Since life itself depends on getting enough to eat, man always has had to procure food before he could even think of doing anything else. Primitive man spent much of his time gathering wild fruits, berries, and nuts. Probably he ate grasshoppers, ants, rodents, and whatever helpless animal life he could get his hands on. Later in the dim centuries of prehistory he learned how to trap animals of larger size and to catch fish. Even today a few isolated aboriginal tribes exist in such a preagricultural society.

Step by step civilized man has improved his food-production efficiency. He learned to save seeds from wild plants and deliberately grow crops. This meant a profound change in his way of life from that based on hunting and the collection of wild fruits. Sometime along the way, man learned to domesticate wild animals and to raise them for meat, milk, fat, and fiber for clothing. The domestication of food crops and the domestication of animals were gigantic leaps forward. They permitted a margin of human effort to be devoted to other things than mere subsistence. It became possible for some members of the clan or tribe to devote themselves to special work for the group—building houses, making clothes, fashioning weapons, or acting as priests to mediate with the mysteries of Nature.

Progress depended mostly on success in producing food and storing large enough reserves to last through the winter months and over bad crop seasons.

For hundreds of generations after the two great technical "break-

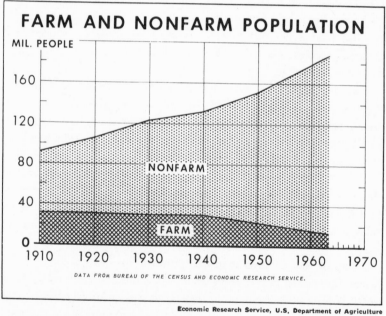

FARM AND NONFARM POPULATION

DATA FROM BUREAU OF THE CENSUS AND ECONOMIC RESEARCH SERVICE.

Economic Research Service, U.S. Department of Agriculture

The number of people living on farms has declined in proportion to our expanding population. Since the early forties, the actual number of farm families has gone down. Today they represent only 13.5 million people, or 7 percent of our population.

throughs" of plant and animal domestication, progress in producing food was extremely slow. At first advancement was made largely by moving to new land or more plentiful natural environments. Later men learned to select seeds from the more productive plants and to breed animals which produced more milk or wool. They developed hand tools and began to use animal power. They learned to rotate crops and to use fertilizer.

But it is well for us to remember that at the time of the American Revolution it still took about 90 per cent of the total work force in America and in the Western world as a whole to produce enough

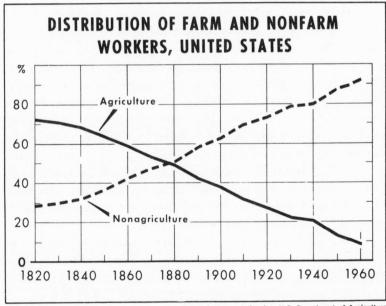

Economic Research Service, U.S. Department of Agriculture

Since the early part of the last century, the percentage of agricultural workers has decreased while the percentage of nonagricultural workers has increased. Today, nonagricultural workers hold more than 90 percent of the nation's jobs.

farm products for the entire society. From this estimate it might seem that the gain in food-producing power from the dawn of civilization to the beginning of the nineteenth century amounted to only 10 per cent of the work time of men. Actually it was more, because farmers performed many other services besides farming. And some produced nonfood crops. But the real gain in food-production efficiency was small—that is evident.

The progress since that time has been at a fantastically more rapid rate. And much of the impetus for this speedup in food production has come from the United States. Walter Wilcox, an agricultural economist with the Library of Congress, says that United States agriculture made more progress in the last 75 years than was made any place in the world in the previous 7,500 years.

The development of the North American continent and the building of the great productive system of America that exists today depended in large measure on success in agricultural production. Food contributes to economic development in three ways: First, good nutrition makes for healthy, energetic workers. Second, increasing food production per man permits the release of manpower for nonfarm industry, services, and other activities. Third, food production in excess of the needs of a country can be sold in foreign markets in exchange for capital goods needed for the growing economy.

The importance of good nutrition to health and vigor has long been known. Ancient peoples knew something about the relationship between a good diet and health, and there are references in the Bible to the effects on strength and vitality of proper foods.

The 1959 Yearbook of the U.S. Department of Agriculture, entitled *Food,* tells about modern research on human nutrition. These studies show by precise measurements that the amount and kind of food eaten by people directly affects the amount of work they can do, their freedom from disease, and their longevity.

Each kind of work activity requires a certain amount of food energy over the amount needed just to maintain life. German studies in the 1940s, for example, showed that the output of miners in the

Ruhr district was directly related to the amount of food energy available, which was controlled by rationing.

A study in 1948 by the State Agricultural Experiment stations in Iowa and Michigan compared the health of sample groups of women and their diets. The women who had the better health were drinking more milk and eating more eggs, vegetables, and whole-grain breads and cereals than the less healthy ones.

Modern scientific research has identified many vitamins, minerals, and proteins that are essential to good health. It is now possible for a country to plan agricultural production and food distribution on the basis of nutritional needs. This is the basis for regulations in many countries regarding the processing of agricultural products. For example, during World War II the United States established a food and nutrition board to provide direction for the national nutrition program. It was evident that many American families were consuming diets inadequate in certain vitamins, minerals, and proteins. The committee proposed adding thiamine, riboflavin, niacin, and iron to white bread flour.

The addition of vitamin A to margarine, the enrichment of milk and other foods for babies with vitamin D, and similar practices are now well known and widely employed in the interests of better diets and better health.

But long before such information was known to scientists, common observation showed that it was important to have plenty of the right kinds of foods. The rapid progress of the United States from an insignificant, underpopulated European colony in the late eighteenth century to the world's leading power a century and a half later has been attributed to many causes but seldom to an abundant agriculture. Yet that, in retrospect, was one of the main factors. Americans were unique in recognizing the importance of agriculture at an early stage.

In addition to supplying the rapidly expanding population with plenty of food, and a well-balanced diet, United States agriculture also was able to produce a substantial surplus for export. Exports of both food and nonfood products were important in earning the foreign

U.S. Department of Agriculture

An evolution in plowing. A hundred years ago, plows were either operated by hand or pulled by livestock, with the farmer walking along behind. Today the farmer usually rides while he drives either a team of horses or,

currency which could be used for purchase of machinery, industrial products of all kinds, and technical assistance from Europe, particularly England. Cotton, tobacco, and other products of southern agriculture were important exports of the colonies and later of the young republic. Later, grain and meat were shipped in large volume from the farms of the developing middle west.

After the Civil War, grain exports from the middle west increased almost annually. Corn exports reached a peak in 1897 with shipment of 212 million bushels, and wheat and flour exports were at a high point in 1901 when the equivalent of nearly 240 million bushels of wheat were shipped. This amounted to about one-third of the wheat produced and about 10 per cent of the corn. These proportions do

U.S. Department of Agriculture

more frequently, a tractor. Left, ox-powered plows on a pioneer farm in the Midwest; right, a riding cultivator drawn by horses.

not seem large. In recent years the United States has exported about half its production of wheat and nearly 10 per cent of its corn. However, exports of meat and meat products, which are made from grain, were a much larger proportion of United States production in the last half of the nineteenth century.

This was a time of rapid industrial growth. But United States factories could not compete with European and British firms in quality or quantity. In the 1870s and 1880s about half of all United States exports were foodstuffs and a large share of the remainder cotton and tobacco. Exports exceeded imports by about $150 million a year, which was a substantial volume of export earnings in relation to the size of the economy at that time. Sale of farm products to Europe made possible the payment of interest on loans from abroad and the borrowing of additional capital from overseas for America's internal development.

Total agricultural exports rose from about $300 million in the fiscal year 1869-70 to $845 million in 1899-1900. This was a period of declining prices. The real earnings of the nation in foreign trade from agricultural products, therefore, nearly tripled in 30 years.

Because plenty of good land was available, but more importantly because of advances in methods of farming which were quickly adopted, United States agriculture was able to increase output per worker steadily.

Not until about 1935 did the farm work force and the farm population of the United States begin to decline in absolute numbers. However, the *percentage* of the work force in agriculture began to decline early in the nineteenth century. Because of agricultural efficiency, it was possible for the natural population growth and immigration to be added mainly to nonfarm employment. This provided the work force for building factories, roads, the whole paraphernalia of a modern industrial economy.

Dr. Earl Heady, professor of economics at Iowa State University, in his book, *Agricultural Policy under Economic Development,* shows how agriculture provided an important amount of capital for general economic progress in America.

In an earlier time, Heady says, the surplus of income from agriculture was practically all in the hands of nobles and landlords. Whatever social investments were made in roads or other public facilities had to be made by the landowners. But in the United States and Canada owner-operators of farms predominated. Surplus or capital was drawn directly from agriculture by property taxes for common purposes. This was true economic as well as political democracy.

Out of it came social overhead capital in the form of schools, roads, courthouses, institutions for the poor and incapacitated, etc.

Agricultural capital also contributed greatly to the development of railroads in the United States. Extension of the rail lines was promoted through federal and state land grants. These land grants were attractive subsidy payments in kind because of the growing market for farm products.

A still more important contribution of agriculture to economic growth came in the supplying of educated people for city occupations. With improving farm efficiency, the population growth of farming areas exceeded the demand for workers in farming. The farming areas invested capital in the education of people beyond the requirement of these areas for labor. This human capital moved to the cities. The cities did not have to allocate investment to the education of this portion of their labor force.

Inheritance customs also caused a distribution of part of the capital gain in agriculture to the cities. Farm children who moved to the urban areas brought with them their share of the family-farm property. In a farm family with three children, it would have been rare even 50 years ago for more than one of them to stay on the farm. Typically, the oldest son might take over the operation of the farm when his father retired or died. The other two children would inherit their third interests in the property on their father's death. This meant that their brother on the farm would have to buy them out or continue to pay them rent. This transfer of capital, along with people, out of agriculture has had an important impact on the development of the nonfarm economy.

There is nothing peculiarly American about this process of economic growth in which agriculture supplies people, capital, knowledge, and foreign earnings for the development of the economy as a whole. The process has been going on since Neolithic times, enabling a smaller and smaller proportion of the population to provide enough food for all. What is significant in the American phase of this story of civilization is the fact that American agriculture improved productivity so rapidly. The transformation of the American economy from a traditional, agricultural one to the world's most advanced technical economy would not have been possible in so short a time otherwise.

The growth of international trade and shipping, the rich deposits of iron and coal, the spur to invention and new technology in all fields, and many other factors have been important in the economic development of the United States. But it should be clear that agriculture has been a prime generator.

5 / AMERICA'S FARM SECRET

IF YOU WERE TO ASK 20 people picked at random in any country (including the United States) the reason why United States agriculture is so productive, at least 15 would answer, "Good land." One or two might say, "Free enterprise." Others might say, "Ambitious and hard-working people."

All these answers are correct. The United States has been blessed with a large amount of fertile land located in a climate which is beneficial for production of grain and other food crops. The free-enterprise system has provided incentives which encourage hard work, saving, and the exercise of initiative to improve the land and increase production.

But many countries have good land, good climate, and hard-working, energetic people. The most important reason for American leadership in agriculture has been something else—the application of science to farming. The United States extended the industrial revolution to agriculture at an earlier date and with more vigor than any other country. It is still doing so.

This is America's farm "secret," a secret which it is glad to share with other countries.

The United States happened to be born at a moment in world history when new ideas about science and experimentation were sweeping the Western world. This was the period of the Enlightenment. There was a new faith in the power of reason.

The revolutionary founding fathers of America were intellectuals fully in tune with the newest thought in Europe. They began to put into practice the ideas of the eighteenth-century European philosophers.

Men like Thomas Jefferson and Benjamin Franklin believed in the infinite capacity of man to improve himself and to improve his works. They believed in the inevitability of progress if reason and scientific principles were applied.

This philosophy was applied to agriculture with special emphasis. Many of the leaders of the new country were themselves farmers or owners of farmland, with an active interest in farming. They helped to establish a wholly new character for agriculture in the fledgling republic.

For hundreds of generations farming had been entirely a matter of tradition. Methods of cultivation were handed down from father to son without question. The idea that farming could be improved was a radical thought that never occurred to the mass of rural people. At the time of the American Revolution, most farmers were still using essentially the methods of farming employed in ancient Rome, with modifications learned from medieval monasteries and from American Indians.

The spirit of change and experimentation led to early and great emphasis on agricultural education. Agricultural societies sprang up. Farming journals were established. Leading men sponsored experiments in farm methods. Travelers searched other lands for new crops and better crops.

Paul H. Johnstone * wrote in *Agriculture*, the 1940 Yearbook of the U.S. Department of Agriculture:

> The United States, at the very outset, developed special institutions directed in one or another way to the service and betterment of agriculture—first agricultural societies of an aristocratic nature, then agricultural societies and fair associations on a more popular level, then agricultural journalism. State boards and de-

---

* Much of the material in this chapter is drawn from articles by Paul H. Johnstone and Everett E. Edwards in the 1940 Yearbook of the Department of Agriculture.

partments of agriculture, national agricultural organizations, a federal department of agriculture and a nationwide system of state agricultural colleges and experiment stations were to follow. In the present day, when such things are taken for granted, their significance is likely to be overlooked. They were in fact, however, something new under the sun. . . .

The existence of a growing body of institutions deliberately and directly devoted to the alteration and improvement of agriculture is therefore a fact of tremendous significance in American history. It has meant that there has been within the agricultural world itself a force constantly working to overcome traditional inertias and to direct agriculture into new paths.

The emphasis on study and new ideas in agriculture began even before the republic was formed. Two resolutions recommending aid to agriculture were adopted by the Second Continental Congress in 1776. In his last annual message to Congress, George Washington advocated a Board of Agriculture to collect and spread information. He proposed "by premiums and small pecuniary aids to encourage and assist a spirit of discovery and improvement." This proposal was approved by a House committee but never came to a vote.

Some of the most famous names in early American history are associated with efforts to improve farming methods. Benjamin Franklin was prominent in the American Philosophical Society, which encouraged the application of science to agriculture and the development of mechanical inventions to save labor in farming. George Washington tried to make Mount Vernon a model farm and carried on many experiments with new methods, new machinery, and new crops. He corresponded with English agriculturists to take advantage of the new methods being developed in England. Thomas Jefferson experimented with crop rotations and other methods of improving soil fertility. He is supposed to have been the first to develop a mathematical formula for a metal moldboard of least resistance for plows.

Agricultural societies that were founded to disseminate scientific information to farmers and to encourage experimentation in farming methods flourished after independence was won. Among them were the South Carolina Agricultural Society (1784), the Philadelphia Society for the Promotion of Agriculture (1785), the New York Society for Agriculture, Arts and Manufactures (1791), and the Massachusetts Society for Promoting Agriculture, somewhat later.

The Albermarle Agriculture Society, founded at Charlottesville, Virginia, in 1817, illustrates the point that the leading men of the new nation were interested in stimulating agricultural progress. Thomas Jefferson was the principal founder of this society and James Madison was later to be its president. Of 30 founding members, there were two future governors of Virginia, a future United States senator and ambassador to Great Britain, a future justice of the United States Supreme

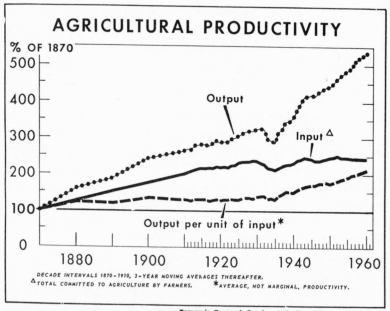

AGRICULTURAL PRODUCTIVITY

% OF 1870

DECADE INTERVALS 1870-1910, 3-YEAR MOVING AVERAGES THEREAFTER.
△ TOTAL COMMITTED TO AGRICULTURE BY FARMERS. *AVERAGE, NOT MARGINAL, PRODUCTIVITY.

Economic Research Service, U.S. Department of Agriculture

The increased output per unit of input—an important result of the application of science to farming in the last hundred years.

Court, a future head of the University of Virginia, a brigadier general, and several others in the top political echelon of the old dominion, in addition to President Jefferson.

These men and their like in the other states instituted agricultural fairs to demonstrate better methods of tillage and of animal husbandry. Livestock fairs had a previous history in the colonies, having been brought over from England. The first agricultural fair of broader scope, more like the county and state fairs of today, probably was held in 1810 in the District of Columbia. President and Mrs. Madison attended. The Berkshire Agricultural Society, organized in Pittsfield, Massachusetts, in 1810, held its first fair in 1811. That sparked development of fairs throughout New England and the middle Atlantic states, and as agriculture moved westward, the educational fair went along with it.

At the same time, farm magazines and newspapers were being established. The *New Jersey Gazette* (1776), the *Rural Magazine* of Newark, New Jersey (1796), and the *Newton Farmers Journal*, also of New Jersey (1797), may have been the first American publications to carry many articles on agriculture. In the early 1800s the *American Farmer* of Baltimore, the *Plough Boy* of Albany, the *New England Farmer* of Boston, the *New York Farmer* of New York City, and the *Southern Agriculturalist* of Charleston began publication. These and many others (by 1850 there were at least 40) were "how-to" magazines, with helpful hints on new methods, scientific discussions, and a strong religious flavor about the virtues of farm life.

While Alexander Hamilton and other Federalists were emphasizing the need for manufacturing and advocating government action to protect infant industries, agriculture was not being neglected. Except for the distribution of public lands to farmers and moral encouragement by government leaders, however, little direct action was taken by government to promote agricultural improvement until late in the nineteenth century. The public-land policies had little to do with the fostering of new technology, but they demonstrated the desire of the country's leaders to expand agricultural opportunities.

Cutting grain by cradle scythe, the common method during the first half of the nineteenth century. Behind each cutter a second man followed to gather the grain and tie it into bundles.

Several presidents and other national officials took action as individuals to advance farm technology. In addition to his other activities on behalf of agriculture, for example, Thomas Jefferson searched Europe for an upland-rice variety and introduced olives into this country.

Agrarian interests had strong influence in the federal government from the beginning. They fought against the policies of Hamilton and other Federalists which seemed to the southern planters and other agrarians to subordinate the interests of 90 per cent of the population, which was agricultural, to the interests of bankers, speculators, and manufacturers. Under Andrew Jackson, the Democratic party championed the cause of small farmers as well as the planters. The Democrats enforced abandonment of property qualifications for voting and office holding and established free public education.

An early mechanical reaper driven by a team of horses needed an even larger team of workers—one to drive, one to ride behind, and a third to rake in and bundle the grain.

In the presidential administration of John Quincy Adams, all United States consuls were directed to send rare plants and seeds back to Washington. Improved breeds of domesticated animals were likewise often sent home by United States representatives abroad. In 1836 the commissioner of patents began to distribute seeds obtained abroad to enterprising farmers. And in 1839 Congress appropriated $1,000 for collecting agricultural statistics, conducting investigations, and distributing seeds.

These cautious beginnings were laying the groundwork for the real push in agricultural research and education which came in the last part of the nineteenth century and the early part of the twentieth. That push started a revolution in farm technology.

The key instrument for this revolution has been a federal-state network of research and education agencies, called the land-grant agricultural colleges. They are called "land grant" because they were established by federal grants of land to the states for the purpose of establishing such institutions.

Farm leaders agitated for education more than for any other one thing during the early nineteenth century. In the 1820s agricultural spokesmen pressed state legislatures for financial aid for agricultural societies and fair associations. The first Lyceum lecture programs were a manifestation of the drive for rural education. They were started by Josiah Holbrook who first tried an industrial school in 1819 and an agricultural school at Derby, Connecticut, in 1824. He conceived the Lyceum idea in 1826, and it proved to be very popular among rural people. By 1831 approximately 900 towns were holding Lyceums, with distinguished lecturers for farmer and small-town audiences.

At the same time public schools were growing in the cities, and reformers were pushing for broader educational opportunities for everyone. In most places, only the children of the well-to-do could attend the private schools. Poor people in the city and farmers in the countryside joined forces to fight for public schools. This was a revolution in itself, since public education, paid for by taxes and run by public bodies, was unheard of in the world. The agricultural journals and agricultural societies campaigned for education, including public schools and specialized agricultural education.

This growing pressure for government support for agricultural education finally led to the establishment of a state university in Michigan, in 1837, as an integral part of the public-school system. The act establishing the university specified instruction in agriculture as an essential element of the curriculum. Because of lack of funds, however, nothing much was done about agricultural education until 1855 when Michigan established an agricultural college separate from the university. Students were first admitted in 1857.

The New York state legislature established a New York state agricultural college in 1853, Maryland did the same in 1856, and Pennsylvania appropriated $25,000 to match the same amount by private subscription for an agricultural college in 1857.

All this was prologue to the first land-grant college bill, introduced by Representative Justin Smith Morrill of Vermont in December 1857, and passed by Congress but vetoed by President Buchanan. Buchanan thought it was unconstitutional and too expensive. The same measure was reintroduced after the Republicans came to power in 1861. It was adopted by Congress and signed by President Lincoln July 2, 1862.

This was an unprecedented act to promote economic development, taken during the depth of the Civil War. It showed the confidence of the nation's leaders that the building of the new nation would go on, and their boldness in departing from the past and seeking new methods.

The Land Grant Act has turned out to be probably the most significant single step by the United States government for the development of agriculture. It has become such a renowned social invention, because of its success in America, that many other countries now are establishing similar institutions.

Representative Morrill was the son and grandson of blacksmiths, a man of rural America, a man of the people. He spurred national action on the idea of public "people's colleges" which would make higher education available at minimum cost for the sons and daughters of farmers and urban working people. He brought to fruition a movement which had been growing for several decades.

Among the newer states with a dedicated interest in agricultural education was Iowa, which had reached statehood only in 1846. Even before the Morrill Act was signed by President Lincoln, three young Iowa legislators, meeting in the capital of Des Moines, presented a bill for an agricultural college to the General Assembly. This was in 1858. The bill passed quickly and was signed into law by the governor. In 1862, after passage of the Morrill Act by Congress, the Iowa General Assembly acted promptly to accept the federal aid. The General Assembly happened to be in special session to consider matters connected with the Civil War. Thus Iowa became the first state to accept the provisions and responsibilities of the Land Grant Act.

Ever since, Iowa State University at Ames has been in the front rank of the nation's land-grant institutions, now numbering 68. It was founded as Iowa Agricultural College and Model Farm. Later its name was changed to Iowa State College of Agriculture and Mechanic Arts, and in 1958 it became the Iowa State University of Science and Technology. These name changes illustrate the changing character of land-grant institutions generally from the early beginnings as pioneer agricultural colleges to well-rounded, genuine universities. Some of the states used their land grants in connection with going universities, as did Michigan, Pennsylvania, and New York, for example. Some established agricultural and mechanics arts colleges as separate institutions, as did Iowa and Oklahoma. Others combined these land-grant institutions with schools of law, medicine, and liberal arts into broad-scale universities right from the start.

But the driving purpose behind the land-grant system was agricultural education and research.

For several years after the Morrill Act was passed nothing much happened. But once the Civil War ended and the work of developing the continent could be resumed, the Morrill Act policy of federal-state cooperation proved extremely effective. The new colleges were to teach "such branches of learning as related to agriculture and the mechanic arts." Up to that time, higher education had been mostly classical education in eastern universities. These new land-grant institutions were to provide practical education for the common man.

Each state received 30,000 acres of public lands within its borders for each of its senators and representatives in Congress. The proceeds from the sale of these lands were to be invested, and the income used to create and maintain colleges.

Early in their history, most of the land-grant agricultural colleges began to look outside the campus to the farming population as a field for education. By the turn of the century, organized "extension teaching" in agriculture was well established. The colleges carried on short courses and extended the knowledge of the campus to farm people through lectures, correspondence, publication of bulletins, demonstrations, and exhibits.

At the same time, these colleges were becoming centers for agricultural research. In 1887 Congress passed a law establishing federal-state cooperative experiment stations to conduct experiments under practical conditions which would be beneficial to farmers. By 1893 the number of these experiment stations had grown to 49.

In addition to the original land grants, the federal government soon began to provide appropriations to help finance the agricultural education system. But not until 1914 was legislation passed setting up a federal-state system of extension services.

We cannot overemphasize the importance to agricultural development of the high value Americans placed on education.

$6\,/\,$ SCIENCE WITH PRACTICE*

FEW AMERICANS, let alone foreigners, appreciate the scope of the public drive for "science with practice" in agriculture in the United States.

The movement was slow in starting, partly because it began in the period of the nation's greatest crisis, the Civil War, and partly because it was such a revolutionary thing. In an age when government was extremely limited and the philosophy of *laissez faire* in economic matters was dominant, the brash, young United States boldly plunged into major government programs for agriculture. The expenditures were not great, but they had enormous effect, because they were "pump-priming" expenditures.

When the federal government spent money, it stimulated spending by the states for agricultural education. Many of the federal government's expenditures are made only on condition of matching expenditures by states.

More important, federal-state research and education primed the pump of private business spending for research and education and development. And still more important, the farming public was infected with the spirit.

In the course of a century United States agriculture has been transformed. Today farmers eagerly seek new ideas and adopt them quickly. But in the early days of the land-grant system, it was difficult

* The title of this chapter is the motto of Iowa State University of Science and Technology.

to get farmers to accept the results of scientific experiments and text-book knowledge.

Seaman A. Knapp, an employee of the Department of Agriculture, probably did as much as any one person to popularize the idea of science in agriculture. He was sent into the southern states to teach farmers how to raise cotton by methods that would withstand the Mexican boll weevil. Instead of just telling farmers what they ought to do, he established demonstration farms to show them. On these farms, farmers could see the improved methods in operation and learn how to apply them on their own farms. As farmers and businessmen observed the results of Knapp's program, they agreed to subsidize agents in their

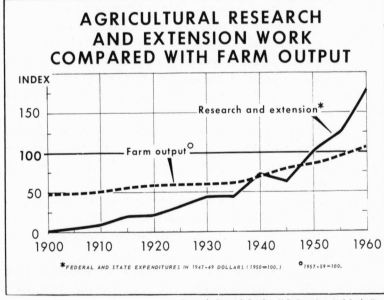

Economic Research Service, U.S. Department of Agriculture

Research and extension work carried on by federal and state governments has expanded rapidly in this century. At the same time, farm output doubled between 1900 and 1957-59.

counties to conduct demonstrations on the boll weevil. This demonstration method spread throughout the country as a practical way of farm education.

The state land-grant colleges found that they could do the work most effectively by establishing county offices. In Broome County, New York, in 1911 a "farm bureau" with a county agent was organized by the local Chamber of Commerce to carry on farm education in cooperation with the land-grant college (Cornell University) and the U.S. Department of Agriculture. This became the pattern of development of extension services throughout the country. After Congress agreed in 1914 to match state grants for extension work, the county-agent system spread rapidly.

The extension services of the land-grant colleges devised new educational methods to overcome traditionalism and spread the gospel of scientific agriculture. In addition to demonstrations, they conducted institutes. They developed a local "leader" apparatus to help the county agent extend his efforts more widely.

The colleges have also made elaborate use of farm newspapers and magazines, their own publications, and radio and television broadcasts. From early in the nineteenth century, America has had a flourishing farm press which has spread new farm information. Since the early 1900s most of the new technical information in the farm papers and magazines has come from the state agricultural colleges.

From the beginning the state agricultural colleges developed a reputation for trustworthiness, accuracy, and disinterested public service. Perhaps more important, they created a feeling of proprietorship for the colleges among their "clients." Farmers in every state refer to "our college" which means the state agricultural college. The agricultural colleges, with their combination of on-campus instruction for young people and off-campus instruction for youngsters below college age and adults, have been able to inspire a warm feeling of participation in the farming population.

More than any other educational institutions, these colleges have concentrated on teaching methods. The idea that education was some-

McManigal, U.S. Department of Agriculture

The steam engine, left, fueled by coal, ran the stationary thresher at right. Inside the thresher the kernels were separated from the wheat and dropped through slats. The chaff and straw were blown up onto the pile behind the

thing set out on a cafeteria line to be taken by those who wanted it was not accepted by the "people's universities" of the land-grant system.

The state agricultural colleges were among the first to organize departments of journalism and of vocational education. Students who were to become county agents and high school agriculture teachers usually were required to take courses in journalism and in teaching methods. Every county agent was expected to write his own news releases. Many a county agent today writes a regular column on farming for weekly and daily newspapers in his county. Hundreds of county agents also broadcast regularly over radio and television.

machine. Fire was always a hazard, and the long conveyor belt kept sparks from the engine away from the readily combustible straw. Right, a close-up of a threshing machine.

The extension services of the land-grant colleges in the beginning worked mainly with the more educated, upper-income farm people. These were the families who joined the extension groups (or "farm bureaus") and cooperated in putting on demonstrations. It was believed that new scientific information would "filter down" from the best farmers to the others in a community.

As institutions of scientific research, the land-grant colleges have since applied scientific analysis to the methods of bringing new ideas to farm people and have learned that the "filter-down" theory works: Farmers are most often influenced to adopt a new method by their own

[59]

neighbors. A farmer may learn about a new method from the county agent or from a newspaper article. But he is most likely to adopt it after seeing another farmer try it or being persuaded by a neighbor.

However, studies show this crude principle needs to be refined. The more highly educated farmers are more likely to adopt a new practice after reading about it. The less educated farmers are more likely to be convinced through personal persuasion by neighbors or friends.

The advance in technology among higher-income farmers has developed a momentum of its own. These advanced farmers no longer rely on the colleges directly for new information. They turn to commercial sources more and more. No "sales effort" by extension is required to get adoption of a new method by the best commercial farmers.

Businesses that deal with farmers are doing much more educational work nowadays. Seed companies, fertilizer companies, meat packers, chemical manufacturers, equipment makers, and livestock-feed companies are spending large amounts on teaching farmers improved methods. Naturally they put their time and money on the commercial farmers, who are a good market.

Farmers who have lacked educational opportunities often need special help in making use of new technology. The land-grant college extension services are directing their attention increasingly to those farmers who have lagged behind. These require more than just knowledge of new methods. They need help in planning the entire farm operation and establishing good accounting records, and they need credit. The federal Farmers Home Administration, which supplies low-cost loans to farmers who cannot qualify for bank credit, has shown the value of direct, supervisory teaching with individual farm families in small groups.

The extension service also started as a demonstration, "show-how" agency, working with small neighborhood groups. This method of teaching is unnecessary for many advanced farm operators in good farming areas now. However, it still is useful in guiding beginning farmers, and in spreading good farming methods among farmers who have been left behind in the technical revolution.

Fifty years ago many states granted subsidies to high schools for introducing courses in agriculture. This movement for practical farm training in high schools culminated in the passage of the Smith-Hughes Vocational Education Act by Congress in 1917. Under this Act funds are given to states to expand their vocational education in agriculture, trade, industries, and home economics. In practice, the major effort has been in agriculture. Agricultural education in the United States has been carried on intensively from the primary grades in school up through the adult years to retirement and even past retirement.

The educators learned early that the best place to start with training in new farm methods was with the youngsters. In the early 1900s the Iowa State College (now Iowa State University) was encouraging formation of boys' and girls' clubs. County superintendents of schools cooperated with the college in formation of these clubs and development of their educational programs.

In 1909 an Iowa county superintendent of schools originated the 4-H clover emblems for boys' and girls' clubs. At first this was a 3-H emblem, standing for head, heart, and hand. Later an extra H was added for health. The 4-H emblem became the official badge of all 4-H club members in the United States.

4-H clubs, organized in every county in the United States, have been a mighty force for improving farm methods. Boys and girls are encouraged to undertake practical projects in raising hogs, beef cattle, dairy cows, poultry; and in crop projects, including corn-yield tests, cultivation methods, fertilization, crop rotation, and so on. The rapid spread of the newest technical developments can be attributed in significant measure to the 4-H clubs.

The vocational agriculture departments in high schools, established under the Smith-Hughes Act, also established boys' clubs, called the Future Farmers of America (FFA). Even more than the 4-H clubs, the FFA has concentrated on farm production projects to help boys learn techniques they could use after graduation in farming for themselves. Many boys in both 4-H club and FFA work have accumulated capital, in the form of money or in the form of high-quality livestock, to give them a start in farming.

The pervasive influence of the agricultural educators has extended into special young people's groups, for those above 4-H-club age, to young married people's groups, and to adults. Agriculture teachers in high schools often have established evening schools for adults, in both agricultural production methods and farm management.

So much public effort in agricultural education could not help but have ramifications throughout rural America. Small-town business-men established funds for promoting 4-H clubs and the FFA. They established prizes for county agricultural fairs and encouraged all kinds of agricultural-improvement projects, such as soil-conservation field days, dairy days, and beef-cattle promotions.

The construction of the farm-education movement in the United States is one of the world's notable examples of public and private enterprise teamwork. Americans went about the task of developing agriculture uninhibited by hairline doctrines about what could be properly done by private enterprise and what by public. This freedom from ideological paralysis has been an important factor in the advance of United States agriculture.

7 / DISCOVERY OF
NEW KNOWLEDGE

A STRONG CASE could be made that the first impetus to the agricultural revolution came from private invention of better tools, making possible the change from manpower to animal power in farming. The agricultural historian Wayne D. Rasmussen divides the agricultural revolution into two revolutions *—first, the adoption of animal power centered about the Civil War and, second, the transition to mechanical power and the adaptation of chemistry to farm production during the World War II period and since. In Rasmussen's first revolution, inventive and enterprising blacksmiths played a major role.

In 1833 John Lane, an Illinois blacksmith, fashioned strips of saw steel over wooden moldboards of plows. John Deere, of the same state, did similar work in 1837, independently of Lane. Deere soon began making plows of wrought-iron moldboards and shares, and by 1857 was turning out 10,000 a year. These plows "scoured," which means they turned the soil cleanly without its sticking to the plow. Other improvements in soil-working equipment came rapidly—along with planting and harvesting machines.

Corn planters were widely used in the west by 1860, and there were a number of different cultivators for corn, all pulled by horses. Grain drills for wheat and oats were patented in these midnineteenth-century years. Mechanical harvesters for wheat and other small grain

* "The Impact of Technological Change on American Agriculture, 1862-1962," *Journal of Economic History* (December 1962).

were replacing the cradle scythe, the hand rake, and even older methods of cutting the grain and gathering it. A mechanical reaper was patented by Obed Hussey in 1833 and another by Cyrus McCormick in 1834. Threshing machines were available by 1840. Every stage of grain production could be performed by machines drawn by horses at the time of the Civil War. Of course it was many decades before the machines were improved to the point of wide practicality and general use.

Rasmussen's second revolution was brought on by the unique American system of agricultural education which provided for parallel institutions of scientific research and public education in agriculture.

State agricultural experiment stations are integral parts of the state land-grant colleges. They are financed by state appropriations and federal grants-in-aid. Usually the agricultural experiment station is located on the college campus. A few states have experiment stations or substations working on special farm-research problems at other locations. But in all cases they are closely related to the teaching of agriculture on the campus and off the campus.

In many states agricultural research scientists are part-time teachers. Because they are closely associated with the users of the new knowledge they discover, agricultural experiment stations are highly practical agencies. Farmers and farm groups bring requests for studies to the experiment stations. Agricultural extension workers see the need for research studies in their contacts with farmers and pass these suggestions along to the research workers in the experiment stations.

The state experiment stations also maintain close relationships with the U.S. Department of Agriculture research service. Many research projects are joint studies between the department and state experiment stations, and federal research scientists often are stationed at agricultural college campuses. But the state stations are not satellites of the federal department, though they receive federal money. They are wholly independent and work with the federal scientists on a cooperative basis.

The Department of Agriculture also operates its own research stations, the main one being the internationally famous center at Beltsville, Maryland. There are regional specialized laboratories in appropriate areas—for example, swine breeding and animal-disease research in Iowa; soybean research in Illinois; vegetable research in South Carolina; sheep-breeding research in Idaho.

The impact of tax-supported, agricultural-science research upon the United States economy cannot be calculated, but it is immense. Every country of the world today is emphasizing scientific research as a foundation for economic development. Modern industries invest great sums in what they call their "R & D" (research and development) departments. American agriculture had such an "R & D" agency many years ago, thanks to the vision of early farm and political leaders.

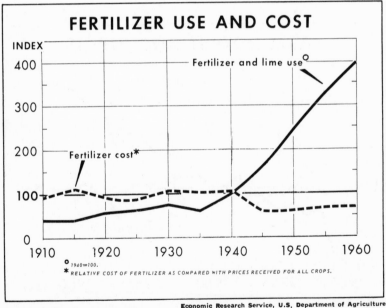

Economic Research Service, U.S. Department of Agriculture

Agricultural research reduces costs for the farmer. While the use of fertilizer and lime has gone up, the cost has gone down. As a result, the farmer raises healthier crops, increases the yield, and conserves the fertility of the soil.

[65]

Scientific knowledge builds on itself. From slow, uncertain beginnings, the accumulated knowledge grows with increasing momentum as time goes on. The last little bit of knowledge to produce a practical result sometimes looms larger in the whole picture of discovery than it should. The long, arduous process of fitting together and classifying knowledge is forgotten. A good example of the typical scientific process is shown by the history of hybrid corn.

Probably the first attempt to use the principle of hybrid vigor in corn breeding was made by W. J. Beal, of the Michigan Agricultural College, in 1881.

From the time the first settlers in New England learned to grow corn from the Indians, seed corn had been selected by farmers from

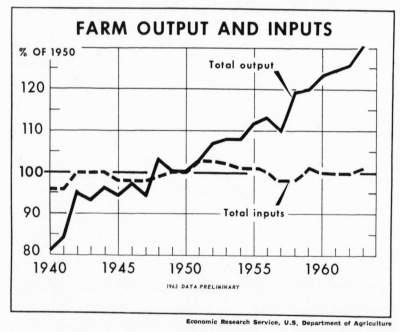

Increases in the total output, while the inputs have leveled off, indicate the efficiency of modern American agriculture.

A 1939 combine, powered by sixteen horses. Before this combined harvester, grain had to be cut two or three weeks before it was ripe to prevent the kernels from falling off. Then the bundled shocks stood in the field until threshing time. With the combine there is no time lapse between reaping and threshing—the ripe grain is cut, swept up into the machine, cleaned, and threshed on the spot.

the best ears. Farmers thought that, by selecting the best-looking ears from the best-looking stalks in the field, they could pass on superior qualities to the progeny and so improve yields. However, open-pollinated varieties are not stable, because of lack of control of the parentage. Windborne pollen fertilizes in a random fashion.

Beal crossed two varieties of corn by detasseling (removing the tassels from) one of the varieties. That variety received pollen, therefore, only from the other variety planted in adjacent rows. Without knowing the reason, men had observed hybrid vigor in animal breeding for hundreds of years. The strong, hardy, spirited mule, hybrid of a donkey and a mare, is the best example of hybrid vigor among common domestic animals. But the same "kick" in growth and vigor from crossing different breeds of horses and other animals was well recognized. Beal's experiment was an effort to apply this principle to crops.

In 1905 G. H. Shull, of the Carnegie Institution, began inbreeding corn, that is, controlled transfer of pollen from an individual plant to the silks of that plant. He was interested solely in theoretical genetics. He wanted to find out whether the number of rows of kernels on an ear was influenced by inbreeding and crossbreeding. By 1908 he realized the practical possibilities of crossbreeding for increasing yields. He recommended inbreeding and crossing of inbred lines for commercial corn production.

E. M. East, of the Illinois Agricultural College, also began inbreeding corn in 1905. Later he moved to the Connecticut Agricultural Experiment Station and continued his research. Like Shull, he demonstrated that corn loses its vigor as it becomes more uniform through successive generations of self-pollination (inbreeding) but that vigor can be regained by crossing the inbred lines. In fact by crossing he greatly increased vigor and enlarged yields.

D. F. Jones, also of the Connecticut experiment station, tried "double-cross" hybrids with four inbred parent lines of corn. This removed a limitation that had made hybrid corn unfeasible commercially. Inbreeding of corn so reduced vigor and yield that crossing two inbred lines was considered impractical. Inbreeding must be repeated for several generations until the particular strain becomes stable. Each generation is selected to maintain the superior types for the particular qualities desired—stiffness of stalk, size of kernels, root strength, etc. A single cross is produced by crossing two inbred lines. Double crosses are the crossing of two different single crosses.

The development of hybrid corn, after Jones's work with double crossing, was contributed to by hundreds of research workers in experiment stations and in private seed companies. Hundreds of inbred lines were isolated and tried out in thousands of crosses. By 1925 several state experiment stations were getting good results. Henry A. Wallace, editor of an Iowa farm paper and later United States secretary of agriculture and vice president, had begun experimentation on his own.

[68]

He developed a cross which was advertised and sold by the Iowa Seed Company in 1924.

A dozen states and the Department of Agriculture established a cooperative hybrid-corn breeding program, exchanging inbred lines and saving much valuable time. In 1926 Wallace established the first seed company for the commercial production of hybrid corn.

As soon as the seed became largely available through both the experiment stations and the commercial seed companies, hybrid corn spread across the United States corn belt like a prairie fire. In 1933 only a fraction of 1 per cent of the land in the corn belt was planted with hybrid seed. Ten years later 78 per cent was hybrid. Today less than 5 per cent of the corn in the United States is open-pollinated.

The development of hybrid corn is the most dramatic food-production story of the century. It resulted in fantastic increases in yield and in efficiency of production. Hybrid corn is bred for uniformity. Stalks are uniform in height. The ears are spaced at uniform height on the stalk for efficient machine harvesting and they are of uniform size and weight. Hybrid corn has been bred for strong stalks and resistance to drought, disease, and insects. Before the introduction of hybrid seed, corn yields had reached a ceiling that could not be lifted, so far as the improvement of corn variety was concerned.

Hybrid seed is produced by careful control of parentage. Commercial seed production is accomplished in isolated fields. The corn tassels are removed from the rows to be used as female parents, before shedding of the pollen begins. Originally crews walked through the fields pulling tassels before the pollen was shed. Later machines were developed to carry the detasselers through the seed fields.

Now researchers have developed male sterile lines of corn which shed no pollen. Fertility can be restored by the incorporation of genes which will accomplish this in the otherwise male sterile lines. By proper manipulation of these traits (male sterility and the trait of restoring male fertility), the seed-corn producer can accomplish the crossing of the chosen lines without the necessity for detasseling. But the hybrid seed corn produced will have full fertility in the farmer's field.

U.S. Department of Agriculture

A far cry from the cradle scythe of a century ago, the modern combine dramatizes several trends in American farming—specialization, efficiency,

Corn is the basic feed grain for livestock in the United States. It is by far the largest crop in total volume and value. The scientific development of hybrid corn, education of farmers in its use, and commercial merchandising of the seed have meant a vast reduction in the cost of meat and other livestock products in the United States.

It is a glittering example of what has happened in many other phases of agricultural research.

The public agricultural research of the U.S. Department of Agriculture and the state agricultural experiment stations produces a constant flow of new ideas, new techniques, new varieties, and new methods of control of disease, insect, and weed.

One of the most interesting of the newer fields of research deals with chemicals and plant growth. Certain chemicals can change the growth of plants, much as animal hormones control the growth and development of animals. Regulating chemicals, such as 2,4-D, can be

U.S. Department of Agriculture

increased output per worker, and dependence on machinery and industrial skills.

used to kill weeds. Other chemicals can be used to change the growth of fruits and vegetables to improve the quality of crops. Regulating chemicals are different from fertilizer chemicals, which furnish some of the building blocks of which plants are made. Regulating chemicals determine to some extent when and how the building blocks are used.

These regulating chemicals can make some fruits, such as bananas, ripen rapidly and develop better flavor. They can make buttons on the ends of lemons stay attached during storage and protect the fruit from rot. Chemical treatment can reduce the cost of thinning crops such as apples. The size of some fruits, such as blackberries and prunes, can be increased by the use of chemicals.

Some plants respond differently to the same regulating chemical. For example, 2,4-D, the weed-killer, can be used to retard the drop of Stayman Winesap apples but is not effective in retarding the drop of McIntosh apples.

[71]

It is not the purpose of this book to tell the fascinating story of agricultural research,* but to make the point that this research is a continued story, that it is heavily financed and operated by public agencies and that it is of great benefit to the general American public.

Neither is it the purpose here to suggest that private invention and development of farm technology have been unimportant.

The federal and state agricultural research stations in this century have created many new mechanical improvements for agriculture. But private manufacturers probably have contributed more. In this phase of agricultural technology, the public institutions have not been the pioneers so much as the stimulators of private invention, and the adapters and educators in use of the equipment. The same could be said of many of the developments in agricultural chemistry in recent years.

In passing lightly over the advances in technology contributed by private individuals and private business firms, the author is not minimizing their significance. The subject of this book is the public policies of the United States affecting agriculture. Hence the emphasis on the part played by public agencies in the agricultural revolution. With all due recognition of the Cyrus McCormicks and the modern corporate innovators, such as International Harvester and Monsanto Chemical Co., public policies and public expenditures established the climate in which the businesses serving agriculture could function most effectively.

For the 50-year period, 1910-60, total public spending for agricultural research in the United States was about $3 billion, measured in 1947-49 prices. Two economists in the U.S. Department of Agriculture estimated that the cost of United States agricultural production in 1947-49 prices over the same 50 years was about $230 billion less than it would have been if agricultural technology had remained at the 1910 level. Not all the improvement in agricultural technology can be attributed to the research of public institutions (though most of it can),

---

* Yearbooks of the U.S. Department of Agriculture provide reports on this research. Some of the information in this chapter came from the 1962 Yearbook, which is titled *After a Hundred Years*.

but these figures suggest the magnitude of the benefits from this investment.

The biggest saving in agricultural cost, of course, has been a saving in labor. Farm output has more than doubled since 1910 and the farm labor force has been cut in half.

As in the case of farm education, public spending for scientific research has stimulated rising private expenditure for agricultural research. In 1959 the total public expenditure for agricultural research was $225 million. Private industry spent about $250 million in the same year, an increase of about $100 million in the preceding decade!

A researcher at the University of Chicago estimated that the annual return on expenditures for research in hybrid corn was in the neighborhood of 700 per cent. Hybrid corn was a fantastically successful project. Other studies requiring equal investment are not always successful, and some which are successful do not pay off so richly.

Earl Heady, of Iowa State University, calculates that there has been a 110 per cent return per year on the total investment in agricultural research and education through public institutions in the last half-century. He added public investment in farm education to the investment in research on the ground that the research would produce no return for the public until it was communicated to farmers. He estimated that in the period of 1910-59 the total public investment in agricultural research and education was $4,145 million. He estimated that the annual saving of "inputs" (costs) was $4,586 million—thus a 110 per cent return *per year* on the total public investment.

The gains have not been confined to improving agriculture itself. Agricultural science cannot be separated from all science. The principles discovered by agricultural research workers in chemistry, geology, botany, and other basic sciences are applied to fields besides agriculture. Agricultural research scientists have made large contributions to human medical research, for example. The methods of insect control, developed for protecting livestock and crops, have proved of value in protecting human health directly.

Millions of people in tropical and subtropical parts of the world have been freed from the dread hookworm disease because research men in the Department of Agriculture found new methods of protecting livestock from injurious parasites. After the mosquito was recognized as a carrier of yellow fever, research studies by a Department of Agriculture scientist furnished information for campaigns to eradicate the insect. Studies of soil for agricultural purposes have added to knowledge of soils for road building, dam construction, and other nonagricultural purposes.

The comparatively small investments that taxpayers have made in agricultural research have been repaid many times over in lower-cost agricultural production, the release of labor for other occupations, the improved quality of food, and the discovery of new uses for farm products.

The public institutions for agriculture in the United States undoubtedly have been well administered. They have been staffed by persons dedicated to the improvement of farm production and of farm life. The success of these institutions as a factor in the total welfare of the country cannot be overstressed. It is the biggest single gift, so far as economic development is concerned, that the United States can offer newer countries which are beginning to develop themselves.

8 / MORE FOOD
FOR LESS MONEY

"AMERICANS ARE the best fed people in the world" has become a cliché—an accepted part of the national puffery and beyond critical analysis. But unlike most such stereotypes, this one is literally true.

Of course this does not mean that hunger and malnutrition are unknown in the United States. It does not mean that improvements cannot be made in supply and distribution of food. It does not mean that all Americans eat the proper amounts of the right kinds of food for good health. But it does mean that enough of the right kinds of food are produced to make possible a good diet for every American. And, despite defects in distribution, by comparison with the rest of the world, Americans have attained food abundance.

If agricultural policy were to be judged solely by performance of the farming industry in production of plenty of food of high quality and wide variety, then United States agricultural policy would have to be judged a matchless success.

The Food and Agriculture Organization (FAO) of the United Nations has made estimates of food consumption country by country around the world. Some of the information on which these estimates are based is dubious, and the FAO experts have had to make "educated guesses." Nevertheless these are the best calculations available and give us rough comparisons of food well-being in various regions of the globe.

If you look at the estimates of total consumption in terms of food energy, you will see that people in many parts of the world have as much to eat on the average as do Americans. In 1958 most of Europe, the Soviet Union, Australia, and New Zealand all had about as many calories per person per day as the United States. Australia, New Zealand, and the United States averaged about 3,200 calories per person per day, while northern Europe and the Soviet Union averaged about 2,900 calories per person per day.

This difference is nothing for Americans to boast about and probably has little significance. In all these well-to-do countries, a great deal of food is wasted. The average person does not need as much as 3,000 calories of food energy per day. Nutrition experts in the U.S. Department of Agriculture say that 2,200 calories are enough on the average. Of course, people doing heavy physical work need more of this body fuel.

It is when we look beyond the crude measure of total calories that we begin to see the basis for the boast about how well fed Americans are. The United States, Canada, Australia, and New Zealand have a much higher proportion of animal protein in their diets than other countries. According to FAO, in 1958 the United States averaged 66 grams of animal protein per person per day—that is, the protein in meat, milk, eggs, poultry, and fish. Australia and New Zealand averaged 67 grams and Canada 62 grams. The western Europeans averaged 41 grams. The Soviet Union, eastern European countries, and Mediterranean countries of Europe averaged about 25 or 26 grams.

There are other significant differences in diets around the world. But this is the most important one—the amount of high-quality animal-protein foods available to the people. Not only is the protein important in itself but also for the vitamins and minerals that meat, milk, and eggs carry. These are the substances so essential to human growth and elimination of deficiency diseases such as rickets. In this matter of animal protein, Americans have reason to be proud and grateful for the performance of their agricultural industry.

The high national *average* consumption, of course, does not mean that every family in the United States receives a good diet. The Department of Agriculture estimated that even with all our food abundance, 1 in 10 Americans early in 1961 was not getting an adequate diet. Many people do not get a good diet because of poor food habits, lack of knowledge of nutrition, or inability to afford enough meat and milk.

A completely adequate diet from a nutrition viewpoint can be obtained with considerably less animal protein than is available on the average in the United States. However, most people if they can afford it prefer to get a high percentage of their protein in meat, poultry, and dairy products. This has been proved in the record of the last 25 years. As incomes have gone up, people have increased their spending for these high-quality protein foods. Meat consumption per person averaged 127 pounds in the years 1935-39 and rose to 161 pounds in 1961. Poultry

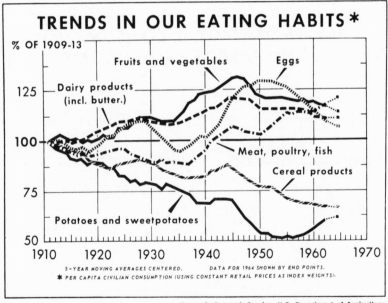

TRENDS IN OUR EATING HABITS *

% OF 1909-13

Fruits and vegetables   Eggs

Dairy products
(incl. butter.)

125

100

Meat, poultry, fish

Cereal products

75

Potatoes and sweetpotatoes

50

1910   1920   1930   1940   1950   1960   1970

5-YEAR MOVING AVERAGES CENTERED.   DATA FOR 1964 SHOWN BY END POINTS.
* PER CAPITA CIVILIAN CONSUMPTION (USING CONSTANT RETAIL PRICES AS INDEX WEIGHTS).

Economic Research Service, U.S. Department of Agriculture

Americans, the best-fed people in the world, are eating more high-quality protein foods and less starchy foods than they did at the beginning of the century. Since 1910 they have bought increasing amounts of dairy products, meat, poultry, fish, fruits, vegetables, and eggs, and a decreasing proportion of grains, cereals, and potatoes.

consumption increased from 16 pounds to 38 pounds, and consumption of dairy products rose from 374 pounds to 393 pounds in the same years.

The food consumption surveys of the U.S. Department of Agriculture show a direct relationship between family income and animal-protein consumption.

The American farmer has made possible this upgrading of diets and at a steady reduction in cost. Some readers might take issue with that statement. They might point out that fresh milk, pork chops, and sirloin steaks all cost more money per pound than they did 25 years ago, or even 15 years ago. That is true, but average family incomes

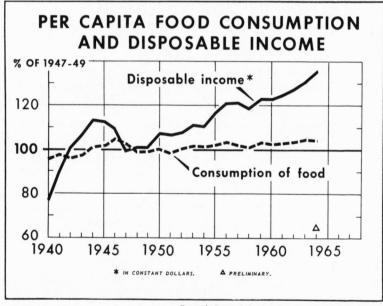

Economic Research Service, U.S. Department of Agriculture

Americans today eat better food with less drain on their incomes than ever before. While food costs have risen only slightly, incomes have gone up at a higher rate. The result: today a smaller part of the income buys the family food.

[78]

have gone up even more. The result is that it takes a smaller proportion of the family income for food now than ever before.

In 1962 about 20 per cent of average consumer income was spent for food in the United States. In the 1935-39 period, about 23 per cent was spent for food. That's only part of the story. The 20 per cent of income in 1962 was buying a much better diet than the 23 per cent in the 1930s. We have pointed out how average consumption of meat, poultry products, and dairy products has increased. The same is true of fruits and vegetables. Meanwhile consumption of starchy foods such as potatoes and cereals has gone down. If Americans were eating the same foods in 1962 as in the 1930s, groceries would have taken only 16 per cent of average consumer income.

It is in this kind of comparison that the performance of American agriculture stands out. But don't Americans pay part of the cost of food in taxes for farm subsidies? Yes, they do, but these subsidies in recent years would add only about 1 per cent to the 20 per cent of consumer income spent for food.

This proportion of income for food is the lowest for any country in the world. In most of the industrial nations, it takes 30 to 50 per cent of the family income to cover the food bill, and in Russia the figure probably is around 60 per cent.

Another way to measure the success of agriculture is to look at the percentage of the national work force required for agricultural production. In many of the less developed countries of the world, from 70 to 80 per cent of the labor force work on farms. In fact, a large majority of the population of the world earn their living by farming. In the industrial countries, the proportion of the work force in agriculture has been greatly reduced. In western Europe as a whole, probably 20 to 25 per cent of the population live on farms. In the Soviet Union, the figure is around 40 or 45 per cent.

But in the United States, less than 10 per cent of the population now live on farms, and only about 7 per cent of the national work force are in agriculture. This figure is the more remarkable, since agricultural exports fully offset agricultural imports.

U.S. Department of Agriculture

One consequence of the machine is that it has replaced many unskilled workers who formerly found employment on farms. Some have moved on to other jobs in agriculture; others have flocked to the cities. Left, hand

The proportion of the United States work force in agriculture is nearly as low as that in England, which imports about half its food supply. Only about 5 per cent of British workers are in agriculture. But to calculate the labor cost of procuring food for the British population, we must estimate the number of workers producing exports of industrial products that are traded for food. Such an estimate might push the British figure up to 15 per cent, as the proportion of the work force engaged in food procurement.

Similarly the percentage in agriculture would have to be reduced for countries such as Denmark, Canada, and Argentina which export large quantities of agricultural products in excess of imports, but all

U.S. Department of Agriculture

picking cotton on a southern plantation in 1879. Right, a mechanical cotton picker that does the work of forty laborers, about twice as many as in the above picture.

such comparisons show the United States in a most favorable position.

American agriculture has freed more than one-third of its labor force in the last 20 years. Output per man hour in agriculture has been going up in the last quarter century at the rate of about 5 per cent a year, as against less than 3 per cent in the rest of the economy. The remarkable rise in agricultural productivity has yielded rich benefits to the consumer.

Here are other comparisons from calculations made by the U.S. Department of Agriculture:

An American farmer in 1963 produced enough food and fiber to feed and clothe, on the average, 27 other persons. Seven years earlier

1 farmer produced enough on the average for 20 persons. Two decades earlier the ratio was 1 farmer to 11 persons. Today 1 farmer can produce what 4 farmers did in the same time shortly after World War I.

Another way to measure the bargain the American consumer enjoys in food is that it takes only 38 hours of work for the average city worker to buy the monthly food supply for the average family (as of 1962-63). In the years 1947-49, it took 60 hours of work to buy the family food supply for a month.

One hour of work by a manufacturing worker in 1947-49 would have bought about 2 pounds of choice beef; in 1961, nearly 3 pounds. An hour's work would buy 6.5 quarts of milk in 1947-49 and would buy 9 quarts in 1962.

Some consumers will dispute these average figures and declare that they are spending more for food than ever before. Actually, they are spending more money for a great increase in processing, packaging, and services that go with food, rather than the food itself. The yearly retail cost of food for the average urban family rose from $940 in 1947-49 to about $1,080 in 1963, an increase of 15 per cent. But the farm value of this food dropped from $466 to $400 in the same period, a 13 per cent *decrease*.

Consumers are buying more and fancier food packaging and more processing, including precooking, and this costs money. More meals are eaten away from home. Men who used to pack a lunch from home now eat in a restaurant. More women work outside the home, also, which increases consumption in restaurants. Meals eaten away from home now account for about $1 of every $4 spent for food.

The Department of Agriculture estimates that in 1962 there was about 30 per cent more service built into each unit of food than in 1940. When consumers buy prepared food, such as meals ready to serve just by heating, they are paying for factory, labor, management, and other costs. The total of these other costs that go with food is considerably larger than the cost of the raw food itself. In 1962, food from domestic sources for the civilian population cost $64 billion. The farm value of these foodstuffs was $21 billion. The processing and marketing bill totaled $43 billion.

With many foods the cost of the processing and marketing takes the major part of the consumer's food dollar, as much as 75 or 85 cents of it. For example, in 1963 the retail price of bread averaged about 22 cents per pound loaf. Of this only 2.4 cents went to the farmer who grew the wheat. All the rest went to the railroads that hauled the wheat, the flour mill, the bakery, and the supermarket. The price of wheat could double and still not add much to the retail price of bread.

Similarly, a quart of milk that sells for 25 cents brings the farmer only 11; a six-ounce can of frozen concentrated orange juice that sells for 25 cents returns the grower 11 cents.

On the average in recent years farmers have received about 40 cents or less of each dollar consumers spend for food. In 1963, 38 cents of the food dollar went to the farmer and 62 cents went for marketing (including processing, transportation, packaging, etc.).

The cost of the raw material in most food items the housewife buys at the supermarket, therefore, is less than the cost of the processing and marketing services. This varies widely, of course, depending on the amount of the services. Fresh meat and fresh vegetables come to the grocery counters with comparatively little handling and packaging. The prices of these foods, therefore, are more closely related to the prices the farmer receives. A moderate change in cattle prices brings a quick change in the price of beefsteak and hamburger, However, the price of canned beef stew will not be adjusted unless the price of cattle has fallen or risen substantially for a considerable period. A freeze in Florida or Texas that cuts the vegetable crops will be reflected immediately in prices of fresh vegetables across the country. But prices of canned string beans and sweet corn will remain the same unless the entire year's production of these canning vegetables falls off.

In general, changes in prices of the raw farm products must be quite large to have perceptible effect on what the housewife pays at the grocery store. She is buying more services than food when she pays her bill at the cashier's counter, and the cost of the services is relatively inflexible. Wages, a big part of the cost, usually are set for long periods by collective bargaining agreements. Transportation rates also are rigid. This relative "stickiness" of food prices at the retail level is becoming more and more true even for the fresh and quick-frozen foods. The housewife wants cleaner, more uniform, better-packaged vegetables, fruits, and fresh meats, and the food merchandisers are providing these services for her. She ought to recognize that the extra money she pays for the services does not increase the return to the farmer.

Only a generation ago many housewives baked their own bread and cakes, canned vegetables, and prepared nearly all the food for the family from raw products bought at the store. Today housewives buy at the store much of the food preparation they used to do themselves —canned and frozen vegetables ready for the pan, baked goods and ready mixes for home baking, and a great variety of "heat and serve" dishes. Because of this, it is difficult for the city food buyer to see how much the cost of food has been lowered. He knows he spends about as much for food as before, but he doesn't realize that more of what he spends is going for "built-in maid service" and other costs rather than food itself.

When the added cost of the increased food services of the last quarter-century is subtracted, it is clear that farmers have been supplying more food of higher quality at lower cost. The reduction in cost of a market basket of the same foods in the last 25 years has been phenomenal.

9 / A NATIONAL ASSET

Is AGRICULTURE a burden or an asset to the national economy and to the national purposes? Agriculture has consistently met the consumption needs of this country—but with a considerable margin to spare. Is this tendency to surplus output a drag on the nation? Is it wholly a waste of national resources? Farm surpluses certainly are troublesome to farmers, and we will discuss these troubles later in this book. But from the national viewpoint, overproduction of farm products has not been without its advantages.

At this point some readers will raise another question, one that has interested philosophers from the beginning of civilization: Is not agriculture so fundamental to national well-being that it must be fostered at whatever cost?

Plato, Aristotle, and other Greek philosophers considered trade and commerce despicable and agriculture ennobling, although they thought the main object of life was to acquire knowledge and not wealth. Roman writers such as Cicero, Cato, and Varro also showed admiration for agriculture and rural life, while expressing contempt for commerce. In the sixteenth century the rise of nation-states and competition among them led to an economic theory called mercantilism. The mercantilists urged government emphasis on exports and limitation of imports in order to accumulate gold which they regarded the basis of national wealth. In the eighteenth century, as a reaction to mercantilism, a group of philosophers in France and England, led by François Quesnay of France, espoused a return to the ancient idea of the superiority of agriculture. These "physiocrats" believed in the supremacy of the natural order and of natural law. They developed a doctrine exalting agriculture as the only true source of wealth, the only industry that yielded a surplus of value over the expenses of production. (They were not thinking of the kind of physical surplus agriculture produces in the modern United States, because in those times all the food that could be produced was certain to be consumed.)

There is a remnant of physiocratic doctrine which continues in the "agricultural fundamentalism" of today. This is the view that there is something unique and peculiar about farming which makes the wealth and welfare of the nation dependent upon prosperity in agriculture. The history of this century dispels this myth conclusively. Agriculture has been a "depressed" industry much of the time during the advancing general prosperity of the post-World War II years. This does not keep politicians from trying to flatter farmers by telling them how important and vital to the country they are. In the 1964 presidential campaign, in a speech in Des Moines, President Lyndon Johnson spoke of economic depressions as "farm led and farm fed," though it was quite obvious that the relative decline in farm income since 1952 had not prevented record nonfarm prosperity.

It would be difficult to show that an industry which today contributes only about 5 per cent of the gross national product could lead the other 95 per cent of the economy either to boom or bust. Agricultural fundamentalism long has been rejected by economists as a valid theory. John D. Black, of Harvard University, wrote in his book, *Agricultural Reform in the United States* (published in 1929):

> It is only a naïve bit of primitive logic that reasons from the fact that we would all starve if we did not have food, to the conclusion that agriculture is the most vital or essential of all industries. . . . In modern complex society, almost all industries are essential. Let any one of the major industries suffer an eclipse and all will be affected.

Though agriculture is not more fundamental than other industries,

[86]

Insecticide

Fertilizer

Herbicide

Seed

With corn, as with other major crops, applied science is the key to a healthy yield. The planter, which is powered by a tractor, combines many operations into one. The seed, at left, is followed by fertilizer, insecticide, and herbicide (weed killer).

[87]

and rural life not inherently more virtuous than city life, we should not overlook the special benefits accruing to the nation because of the exceptional productivity of American agriculture. In one sense American experience has lent some substance to the physiocratic beliefs about surplus value in agriculture. In this century of world revolution and war, the extra capacity of our farming industry has been and will continue to be an important asset to the country.

First, consider the unmatched ability of this country to use food as an instrument of foreign policy.

America traditionally has been known as a country ever ready to come to the relief of famine-sufferers anywhere in the world. In the wars, revolutions, and famines of the twentieth century, the United States has supplied food to the hungry in China, in Russia, in India, and many other countries, without regard to political considerations. In recent years, with the tremendous increases in farm production, the United States has been in a stronger position than ever before to aid other countries needing food. Instead of merely meeting emergency famine situations, we have been able to employ food as a form of development assistance for newly independent countries.

In his 1963 message to Congress on agriculture, President Kennedy reported:

An increasingly important tool of American foreign policy—and of particular significance to our mutual assistance and development effort, including the Alliance for Progress—is the Food-for-Peace program. It is now being expanded to assume a larger share of the cost of mutual assistance. We make a grave mistake if we regard Food for Peace as merely a program for disposal of surplus commodities instead of an opportunity to utilize our agricultural capacity to encourage the economic development of new and developing nations.

In the past year, Food-for-Peace exports of wheat and flour alone filled an average of three 10,000-ton cargoes moving overseas daily. We are reaching more needy overseas than ever before—92 million people a day, including 35 million school children and two million pre-school children. During the past six months we have undertaken to supply food as part payment for wages to 2.4 million people working on self-help projects for economic development in seven countries. I am recommending in the 1964 budget $1.9 billion for continuation of the Food-for-Peace program.

Some foreigners (and some Americans) take the cynical view that Food for Peace is "merely a program for disposal of surplus." Unquestionably the sale overseas of surplus farm products at concessional prices and the donations of food to foreign countries have been beneficial to American farmers. The reason for this is that the demand for most farm products in the United States is extremely inelastic. A small increase in the total supply means a drastically lowered price to farmers. Naturally farmers are glad to "get rid of" a surplus that would depress prices for their entire marketings.

The motivation for the donation of food to other countries may not be entirely altruistic. But to conclude that Food for Peace is nothing but "dumping" America's farm surpluses would be a mistake, as President Kennedy said. It would be far cheaper and simpler not to produce the surplus. This would involve strict production controls by government.

It is true that controls are unpopular with farmers and objectionable to the American public as measures in conflict with free private-enterprise philosophy. So Food for Peace is a convenient way to meet the surplus problem. But this is not a full explanation. The humanitarian motive behind using America's food bounty to help others always has been important. "There is no surplus as long as people are hungry" is not just a slogan but a deeply felt belief of many Americans.

Regardless of motives, no one can deny that the Food for Peace program has been beneficial to many countries. It has helped to improve diets and has contributed to economic development. Aid in the form of food is only one detail in a development program, to be sure. Much more is needed in the form of direct money assistance, industrial equipment, transportation equipment, and so on. However, the late Prime Minister Jawaharlal Nehru of India said that food supplied by the United States was the most important form of foreign aid received by his country.

One of the bedrock principles of United States foreign policy is that great disparity in wealth among nations makes for an unstable world. Therefore the United States seeks to improve the economic welfare of less developed countries that have low production and low income. We are living through the disappearance of the colonial empires of the eighteenth and nineteenth centuries. New independent countries are arising, and the peoples in these countries believe they can have the good things of life enjoyed by Western countries.

It is easy to see the importance to the United States of an abundant agricultural industry in carrying out a policy of aid to such countries. These new countries are predominantly agricultural. In order to make progress and advance their incomes, they must become more efficient in agriculture to free labor for other kinds of production. Not only can American agriculture supply surpluses of food, it also can supply technical knowledge, research help, and the lessons from its own experience for the newer countries.

In the worldwide competition between the Communist movement and the democracies, America's bountiful agricultural industry becomes a tremendous asset. In the field of agricultural development, the United States is far ahead of the Soviet Union and other Communist countries. The United States has available a vast research and educational system in agriculture which can be used to help other countries.

Private educational foundations began to supply agricultural know-how to other countries shortly before World War II. The work of the Rockefeller Foundation in Mexico has been particularly outstanding. In 1943, in the middle of World War II, the Rockefeller Foundation began research studies in Mexico, at the invitation of the Mexican government, to develop improved strains of important food crops. Rewarding progress in improving food production in Mexico has resulted. Wheat and corn are now plentiful to meet demand for cereals for human food, and larger amounts of corn are becoming available for feed to livestock. The potato was once a luxury food in Mexico because of the disease problem. It is now being added increasingly to the general diet, as a result of development of disease-resistant strains.

Following the lead of the private foundations, the United States government has been steadily expanding its technical agriculture assistance to other countries. During World War II, the government began research programs in several other Latin American countries to help improve food production. The results have not been as spectacular as in Mexico, largely because of political and social reasons. Getting better seed varieties in the laboratory is one thing. Getting the better seeds used on the land is another.

A combination of land reform, general education, better markets, adequate farm credit, and stable government is needed along with the scientific research to enable agriculture to advance rapidly.

Productive as American agriculture is, its potentialities have hardly been touched. The Department of Agriculture estimates that if all farmers applied technical knowledge as fully as the top 25 per cent of farmers do now, food and fiber production could be doubled. This reserve of production capacity is a much greater asset to the United States than the stored reserves of grain, cotton, dairy products, and other farm commodities on hand at the moment. If farmers were called upon to expand production and were supplied with the necessary amounts of fertilizers, gasoline, machinery, and other production goods, they could easily push output up at a rapid rate.

Even under present government programs attempting to restrain farm production, output is expected to grow faster than demand.*

At a time when farmers are worried about surpluses which result in low prices to them, it may seem strange to talk about surpluses and surplus capacity as an "asset." But that is only because memories are short. Twice in this century American agriculture has been called upon to fill the extra food requirements of a world war. In 1934 and again

* See *Farm Production: Trends, Prospects and Programs,* Agriculture Information Bulletin No. 239 (U.S. Department of Agriculture, 1961).

in 1936 severe droughts struck much of the middle west and the Great Plains, resulting in drastic reductions in crop production, severe damage to pasture and range land, and reductions in livestock production.

Such emergencies can occur again. In recent years the government has been carrying reserves of farm products valued at $7 to $9 billion. These reserves seem top-heavy and extremely costly, but they might turn out to be of great value, just as the much smaller reserves of 1938-41 were when World War II began.

The value we place on agriculture's reserve capacity and its large inventory of staple foods and fibers depends on the state of world tensions and our fear of war.

At the peak of the surplus accumulation in 1961, before that year's crops were harvested, the nation had approximately one-half of a year's supply of corn in reserve (about 2.0 billion bushels) and more than a full year's supply of wheat (about 1.4 billion bushels) for both home consumption and exports. That seemed to be far more than a safe reserve of grain. Both corn and wheat are flexible raw materials that can be used for a variety of purposes for direct human consumption or feeding to various kinds of livestock. They are in large measure interchangeable in their uses. By careful planning and frugal use, the grain stockpile could carry the nation through several years of short production. The inventory could be stretched if necessary by using it for human consumption instead of "processing" it through livestock into meat, milk, and eggs.

But several years ago when the peril of nuclear war seemed greater than it does as this book goes into publication, proposals were made by some advocates of maximum civil defense for a large increase in food stockpiling. Dr. Edward Teller, the nuclear physicist, for example, felt the nation should undertake a massive underground shelter program, with much larger reserves of food. Three billion bushels of grain did not seem too much to those with Dr. Teller's views.

Of course, if the decision were made to construct costly shelters to protect the population against radioactive fallout, adequate food reserves would have to be provided also. It would not make sense to

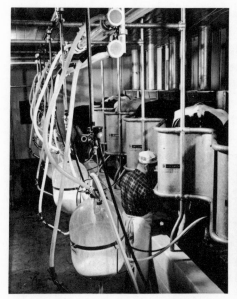

Grant Heilman   Des Moines Register and Tribune

Machines that make farming more efficient are found on practically every type of farm. On dairy farms the pail and stool have been replaced by automatic milkers. Feeding livestock, a job formerly done by hand, has been simplified by the worm or screw feeder, which brings silage directly from the silo to the feeding trough.

invest the money in shelters without investing in food also. Nuclear attack on a major scale would paralyze production of farm crops and livestock for one growing season at least, even if it did not contaminate soil for the next season.

This writer is not advocating such a civil-defense program. But conception of civil defense in such dramatic terms helps to show that the large inventories of farm products carried as surplus by the government have some public utility. The cost of carrying this reserve should not be charged entirely as subsidy to agriculture. Like the Food for Peace program, it has a value to the nation as a whole, and our public accounting should take cognizance of it. The surplus makes for a serious problem in maintaining good incomes for farm people. It is a threatening backlog hanging over the market.

But it should be a matter of comforting assurance to the 90 per cent of the people who live in towns and cities that there is virtually no danger of food shortage in America. In man's long history, this never has been accomplished before. It is something entirely new in the world, and most people are not quite aware of it yet.

While we are talking about agriculture's contributions to the society at large, let us mention briefly two more. These are agriculture's stability of production and its responsiveness to the tastes and demands of consumers.

At first glance these two contributions may seem to be in contradiction. However, what we mean by stability of output is the total production of all United States agriculture from one year to another. The "mix" of this output may vary considerably depending on what consumers want.

No other industry can match farming in stability of production. This is partly because the United States is a big country where ups and downs of production of some crops in localized areas offset one another. It is partly because new technology reduces, to some degree, the effect of weather as a cause of crop failure. For example, farmers with modern equipment can do their planting within a few days and do not get "caught" by bad weather, as they would if the planting were stretched out over several weeks. Still another reason for stability of output is that agriculture is an industry of many small business firms. There is little or no coordination of production plans, although government programs help for some crops. Thus each producer grows as much as he can, and the industry as a whole maintains steady, slowly rising output, regardless of prices or demand.

For the same reason—that is, because the industry is highly competitive, with a large number of small business firms—agriculture responds quickly to the demands of consumers. Increased demand for meat, particularly beef, since World War II has brought forth a very substantial rise in production of beef cattle. In manufacturing industries that are concentrated into a few large firms, such an increase in demand would be met by moderate increases in production and substantial rises in prices, because the industry could control its rate of increase in production. In agriculture competitive forces really work to the benefit of the consumer. Only in a few commodities, produced by relatively small groups of farmers who are well organized into marketing associations, do farm producers have significant control over production or prices.

Farming does not deliver sudden, disrupting shocks to the economy, as for example the metal-working industries often do. Farm production continues to advance steadily, and farm employment does not go up and down violently from one year to another.

Even when farmers' incomes are going down, as they were during the 1950s, farm production is maintained. Purchases of fertilizers, gasoline, drugs, insecticides, and other production supplies from nonfarm industry do not fall off. What happens is that farm families reduce their purchases of consumer goods. But this has comparatively little effect on the economy as a whole. In their main purchases from the nonfarm economy, production supplies, farmers provide a fairly stable market at all times. Agriculture, an industry made up largely of self-employed small businessmen, does not throw a hundred thousand men out of work and onto public relief programs, as do major manufacturing industries, as the result of strikes or other work stoppages or because of slack demand. Farmers do not quit producing when prices are unfavorable. They do not go on relief or receive unemployment compensation. They have no choice but to produce.

Thus agriculture, in addition to providing abundance of food for consumers and a surplus for aiding foreign countries, is a stabilizing force in the modern industrial economy.

*10 / * THE FARMER'S
DISADVANTAGE

AGRICULTURE HAS MADE a large contribution to economic development of the United States. Farmers have responded well to the public investment in new farm methods and have rapidly increased production. The public has benefited from cheap and abundant food and from the release of labor from farming for use in other work.

Our national agricultural policy has been a brilliant success except for one thing: Farmers have not shared in the benefits created by their own productivity. Their average income has remained far below the average for the nation as a whole.

In three of the four decades from 1920 to 1960, income per person in farming was about one-half the income per person of the nonfarm population. In the wartime forties, farm income rose in comparison with nonfarm income. The voracious demands for farm products to feed Allied armies and starving populations in the wake of war pushed prices of farm products upward. Except for that decade of war and postwar relief, however, American agriculture has been plagued with overproduction, surpluses, and low prices.

In most countries the farm problem is one of scarcity, but in the United States and Canada, and increasingly in other technically advanced countries, the problem is surplus.

With farming an industry of many small firms, no individual farmer can have appreciable influence on total production or total marketings. Each farmer, operating on his own, has no choice but to produce as much as possible at all times. Whatever the price level, he maximizes his own income by producing at the maximum. Even in a serious economic depression, such as during the 1930s, farmers maintain or increase production. Theoretically if hard times lasted long enough to force many farmers out of business, agriculture might reduce production. In practice even the most prolonged depression of prices we have ever experienced has not caused a reduction in farm production.

The constant upward drive to farm production from the competitive nature of the farming industry has been reinforced by the public programs of research, education, soil conservation, land reclamation, and easy farm credit.

During both World War I and World War II the American farmer was called upon for a large expansion in production. United States agriculture was the chief reliance of the Allies for meeting wartime food needs.

In both wars, but especially the second, the rise in farm production was phenomenal. Government made available machinery, gasoline, fertilizer, and other farm supplies. It protected the farm labor supply by draft exemption and other means. It permitted prices of farm products to rise sharply, and farmers were guaranteed minimum prices.

But when the extra demands of wartime subsided, production could not be turned off. At the end of World War I, prices of farm products collapsed. That is when the expression "farm surplus" began to get into political debate in America. Production continued at wartime levels, though markets were clogged and exports fell off. There were demands for farm relief, with a variety of proposals for government action to support prices and restrain production.

At the end of World War II, the situation was somewhat different. In the first few years after the war, the booming demand for farm products continued. The United States poured billions of dollars into relief and rehabilitation of the wartorn countries of Europe, and much of this money was spent for American grain and other farm products.

In the 1950s, however, while the general level of prosperity remained high, the old problem of too much agricultural production re-

During the last few generations, the picture of the farmer walking behind his plow has all but disappeared from the American scene. But, in spite of rapid technological changes, some farmers, like this one, still eke out their existence by the old, inefficient methods.

appeared. Farm production continued to advance rapidly as a wave of new technology was adopted by farmers. Despite high consumer-purchasing power and growing markets, including large exports, prices of farm products began to fall. Production was increasing faster than the demand for farm products.

One side of the farm commercial problem is the tendency to advance production continuously. A spurt of new technology, a wartime campaign for more food production, a sharp rise in prices of farm products may push farm production to a new high plateau. But nothing seems to bring production down off that plateau. Advances in farm output seem to be irreversible.

[99]

The other side of the farm-market equation is that the demand for food is not advancing as it did in earlier years. People are so well fed in the United States now that they do not demand more food as they increase their incomes. Sixty years ago rising city incomes meant a bigger market for farm products. But today consumers are more likely to use extra income for autos, TV sets, vacations. They may spend a little more for higher quality food, but increases in such spending no longer are a substantial factor in farm income. Consumers spend more money for the *things that go with food* when their incomes rise. That is, they buy more precooked meals, restaurant meals, and other services with food. But they don't spend more for the food itself.

Because they have little or no control over the total supply of farm products, farmers have little bargaining power in the economy. Hundreds of thousands of farmers produce the major commodities. It is impossible for them to act in concert to adjust production to demand without the help of a centralizing agency, such as the government or, conceivably, a private cartel of marketing cooperatives.

It would be to the advantage of farmers collectively if production could be tailored to market requirements. With demand for agricultural products so inelastic, a small increase in supply means a substantial decline in prices. For all farm products as a group in the United States, an increase in supply of 5 per cent results in a decrease in prices of about 20 per cent. Thus a modest expansion of supply above normal market needs—in the absence of group action to store or divert the surplus—reduces the gross income to agriculture. A large grain crop or a large supply of hogs for slaughter sells for less total money than a small supply.

`The individual producer feels helpless in such a situation, and he is. No matter what he does he can have no effect on the total supply or on the price. Once his capital is committed to specialized farm production, it has relatively little value for use outside of agriculture. To continue to use the capital equipment for production, even at low prices, results in less financial loss than not to use it or to reduce production.

Farmers often can shift from one crop to another, for example from corn to soybeans, depending on the price outlook. Or they can change from feeding corn to hogs to fattening beef cattle or to selling the corn on the market for cash.

But for an individual producer to reduce his total volume of production does not make sense, regardless of the price level. This assumes that he is a full-time farmer, intending to continue in the business.

If times get tough enough he may leave farming, of course. Or in some situations he may find it possible to reduce his farming operations and take a part-time job in a factory or in some other nonfarm work. But by and large, for agriculture as a whole, production does not fall. The theory of the market—that production will decline in response to a reduction in prices—simply does not work out. The "automatic regulator" of free-market theory does not regulate agricultural production downward in a modern industrial economy—only upward.

On the other hand, the farmer is confronted with an inflexible price situation for the goods he buys for use in production. Most nonfarm industry is able to adjust production downward when demand declines in order to prevent an inventory pileup and to maintain a fairly steady price level. Costs of farm production supplies, such as gasoline, machinery, chemicals, and fertilizer, do not decline in proportion when the farmer's gross income declines. The farmer sells in a free, competitive market of the classical variety with many small firms, each incapable of market control. The farmer buys in a new kind of market, often dominated by a few large firms, where competition tends to be in quality, service, and advertising, and not in prices.

The tendency has been for a gradual but persistent rise in the cost of things farmers buy for use in production during the years since World War II. Meanwhile farm production has been growing and prices of farm products declining. So the farmer is faced with a squeeze between the prices he receives and the prices he pays. During the decade of the 1950s the purchasing power of a unit of farm products shrank by one-fifth as measured in terms of the things farmers buy.

Between 1947-49 and 1957-59 total farm production increased 21 per cent. But gross farm income advanced only 9 per cent, and the net realized income of farm operators *declined* by 25 per cent.

There were one million fewer farms in 1959 than in 1949, so fewer farm families shared the reduced income. Farmers with annual sales of $2,500 or more, who are classified as "commercial" farmers, had net incomes from farming averaging about $5,200 in 1950. At the end of the decade, their net incomes had dropped to an average of $4,200.

If income from nonfarm sources is included, these commercial-farm families averaged about $6,000 at the start of the decade, compared with an average of $5,300 for all nonfarm families. This is comparing the "upper crust" of farming with all the rest of the United States population.

In 1959 average income of these commercial farm families, including income from nonfarm sources, had dropped to $5,800. But the average nonfarm family income had risen to about $7,600.

Thus for doing an excellent job of production, improving efficiency, and releasing labor to other occupations, farmers suffered a loss of income during the 1950s. It should be remembered that this loss occurred despite a considerable array of federal farm price-support and subsidy programs. Without these programs, farm income would have been far lower.

11 / THE FAMILY FARM TODAY

WHAT ABOUT THE FAMILY FARM in the United States today? Is it still strong? Or are large-scale, factory-type farms taking over? And what about land ownership: Are the farms coming into the ownership of large landlords who operate them with tenants, squeezing out the small landowner?

While the family farm has been a prime objective of public policy in the United States throughout its history, we must recognize that there also have been conflicting concepts at work. One such conflicting concept has been the right of every individual to acquire as much land as he could. Even when the 160-acre homestead movement was at its height, many large tracts of land were sold or given to railroads, other corporations, and individuals. There never has been any restrictions on consolidation of homesteads into larger farms.

The Homestead Act, with its emphasis on 160-acre parcels, was out of date soon after it was enacted. The 160-acre farm was reasonable and practical in the eastern states and the middle west as far west as the Missouri River. But most of these states already were occupied by the end of the Civil War.

The new lands to be opened for homesteading were in the Great Plains and farther west. In these areas, with rainfall averaging from 10 to 18 inches a year compared with 30 to 40 inches east of the Missouri River, the small homestead was not practical. Effective farming required grazing, dry-land farming (with fallow years), or irrigation. This usually meant larger land units than the Homestead Law provided. Production per acre, of grain, pasture feed, and livestock, is much lower on the semiarid plains than on the well-watered lands east of the Missouri. So a man must have more land in such areas to earn the level of income he could earn on a smaller acreage in Iowa or Illinois.

The force of new farm technology generally has been in the direction of encouraging larger farms. The inventions of the multiple-bottom plow, the reaper, the corn harvester, the combined harvester, and above all, the tractor, made it possible for a farmer to handle increasing acreages of cropland.

The number of farms in the United States has declined very rapidly in the last quarter-century. At the outbreak of World War II, American agriculture was organized into 6 million farms, with more than 30 million people living on them. In 1960, there were only about 3.7 million farms, with 13.5 million people.* The average size of farm increased very rapidly during the last three decades and was about 325 acres in 1961. This compares with 134 acres in 1880 and 174 acres in 1940.

Acreage alone is not a good measure of size of the farm business. Farms have been growing larger not just in area but also in amount of production and volume of sales. The number of farms with value of production $10,000 or more per year increased from 484,000 in 1949 to 794,000 in 1959. During the same 10 years the total number of farms dropped from 5.2 million to 3.7 million. The number of farms producing less than $10,000 worth of commodities declined from 4.7 million to 2.8 million.

A typical high-production corn-belt (midwestern) farm specializing in hog raising and the fattening of beef cattle in 1959 had a total capitalization of about $83,000. The gross income on that farm was nearly $25,000. The operating expense (including a charge of $4,300 for interest on the capital) was $18,000 and the net farm income was

---

* Intercensus estimates of the U.S. Department of Agriculture indicate a further decline to about 3.4 million farms in 1964 and farm population of 13.4 million in 1963.

$6,600. Assuming the farmer owned all the capital, his net income was $10,900 ($6,600 plus $4,300).

This "typical" farm is not a real farm but an average of several real farms of the most common sizes of the hog-beef type in the corn belt. The farms were selected by the U.S. Department of Agriculture. A comparable farm had net income of about $10,000 in 1949.

A similar composite farm, typical of dairy farms in western Wisconsin, had an investment of only $31,000, gross farm income of $8,300, operating expenses of $4,900, and net farm income of $3,400. In 1949 such a farm had gross income of about $7,000 and a net of $3,200.

A typical winter-wheat farm in the Kansas-Oklahoma-Texas area in 1959 had a total investment of about $90,000. Where the livestock farms of the corn belt have much of their investment in cattle and hogs, this farm has most of its investment in land and buildings. This average wheat farm was nearly 600 acres in size. It had a gross income of $13,-400 and a net income of $7,800, about the same as in 1949.

In contrast a typical North Carolina tobacco and cotton farm in 1959 had an investment of $25,000, gross income of $7,200, operating expenses of $4,600, and net farm income of $2,600, also about the same as in 1949.

A large-scale Mississippi delta cotton farm, with investment of $150,000-$200,000, returned net income of more than $20,000 per year in 1949 and continued at this level through most of the 1950s.

From these few examples, we can get a picture of the great variety in size and kind of business in commercial agriculture in the United States. Some types of farms have been increasing in size of business in recent years and some have not. Technical changes in some crops have not been such as to cause further increases in farm size. Also, crop acreage allotments under government programs have tended to keep some types of farms from growing in size.

Yet despite increasing size for most types of farms, increasing commercialization and increasing specialization of farms, the family farm is not fading out but seems to be fully holding its own.

John M. Brewster, an agricultural economist for the U.S. Department of Agriculture, took as a dividing line between family farms and larger-than-family farms 1.5 man-years of hired labor. The available labor force of a farm family is estimated to be about 1.5 man-years. If a farmer hires 1.5 man-years or more *in addition,* this, according to Brewster's definition, is a larger-than-family farm.

If family farms were on the way out, the farms on which families do most of the work would be accounting for a smaller proportion of all farms. They also would be accounting for a smaller proportion of total farm marketings. Hired labor would be making up a larger proportion of all work done on farms. These things have not been happening.

Farms using less than 1.5 man-years of hired labor (that is, family farms) made up 96 per cent of all farms in 1954. They made up 95 per cent of all farms in 1949. All available indications point toward a maintenance of this proportion since 1954. Family farms sold 74 per cent of all farm marketings in 1954, as compared with 70 per cent in 1944. This trend also seems to have continued since 1954.

From 1948 to 1959, the amount of work done by hired labor on United States farms declined 39 per cent. The amount of work performed by family members declined 35 per cent.

Since World War II the number of family-type farms has been declining rapidly, just as the number of farms in general has been falling off. However, most of the reduction in number of family farms has been of the very small farms with inadequate income.

Let us take $10,000 per year as an arbitrary measure of the value of marketings from a farm which could be considered "adequate." (Net income of course is much less, on the average less than half as much.) In 1949 the census reported 334,000 family farms (using less than 1.5 man-years of hired labor) with total marketings of $10,000 or more. In 1954 there were 440,000 such farms, and in 1959, 680,000. Thus in 10 years the number of these "adequate" family farms increased by 104 per cent.

In the same 10-year period, the number of "inadequate" family

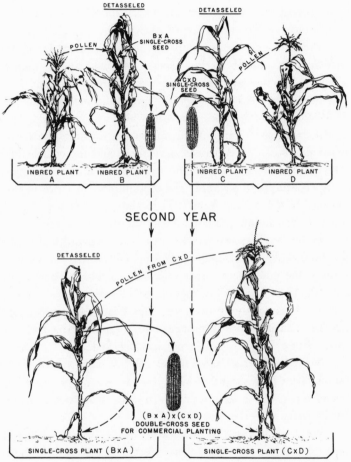

The development of hybrid corn has completely revolutionized our nation's largest crop by improving its quality, yield, and resistance to disease. The initial crossing (top) is done by detasseling an inbred variety and fertilizing it with pollen from another variety. The process is repeated the second year (bottom), but this time with two single-crossed plants.

farms, that is with marketings below $10,000, declined by 50 per cent.

What has been happening to the larger-than-family farms? In the same period the number of larger-than-family farms declined from 150,000 to 114,000, a decrease of 24 per cent.

From these figures it is apparent that "adequate" family farms are increasing in number at the expense of "inadequate" family farms. They are also increasing at the expense of larger-than-family units.

Studies by the Department of Agriculture indicate that the figure of $10,000 gross farm sales in a year, which we have used as a measure of the "adequate" family farm, marks the dividing line between the expanding sector of American agriculture and the contracting sector. This was the dividing line in the 1950s, but it has been rising as technology continues to advance. The total number of farms in the nation declined by 2.4 million from 1939 to 1964, according to U.S. Department of Agriculture estimates. About 95 per cent of this decline is explained by the disappearance of very small farms with annual sales of less than $2,500 (measured in 1959 prices). During the same quarter-century the number of farms with sales of $10,000 and above more than doubled. Yet the average value of sales of these $10,000-plus farms increased only 20 per cent. This is another proof that the expansion is taking place in proficient-sized family farms and not in the huge "factory" farms, as is commonly believed.

Nevertheless the United States still has many more "inadequate" family farms than the other kind. Trends in farm organization are in the direction of stronger family farms, but many weak and insecure family farms still exist.

What will happen to these farms in the future? They will either be combined into larger and more effective family farms or into larger-than-family farms. On the basis of changes at the end of the decade of the 1950s, we can feel that the development will be toward the traditional family farm more than in the direction of the larger-scale "corporate" farm.

The national averages we have been using hide changes that are taking place in different regions and among different types of farming.

To produce hybrid corn, carefully selected inbred lines are detasseled before the pollen begins to shed. The detasseled plants are then fertilized with the pollen from other inbred plants. After its development, hybrid corn spread rapidly and widely throughout the country: in 1933 less than one percent of all corn produced came from hybrid lines; today more than 95 percent is hybrid.

Hi-Bred Seed Company

In the general farming regions of the eastern states and the corn belt, the introduction of new machinery and improved technology clearly has buttressed the independent family farm. It has reduced the need for hired labor.

I can think of farms in my native state of Iowa, for example, that employed three or four men in the 1930s but hire none today. A farmer with a 240-acre farm in 1935 could hardly get the work done without hiring two or three men to help him at planting time, during the corn cultivation period, and during both small-grain and corn harvesting

[109]

periods. Probably he had a full-time hired man to help with the live-stock chores the year round, and if he had a big livestock program, he might have two full-time hired men.

Today it is unusual for the average farmer on that size farm to have more than one full-time hired man. Many such farms are operated entirely by the farmer himself without hired help. He needs no additional help to plant corn. Nor does he need extra labor during corn cultivation, small-grain harvest, or corn harvest. The only reason he would hire extra help nowadays, ordinarily, would be for work with the livestock.

In the large fruit- and vegetable-growing regions of the middle Atlantic coast, Florida, the other Gulf states, the southwest, and California, the picture is not the same. In these regions, very large-scale farms are more common, and large numbers of seasonal hired workers are employed. Many of these workers are migratory, and a considerable number of them have been "imported" from Mexico and the Carib-bean Islands. These alien workers were paid much higher wages than they would be in their homelands and were glad to earn the extra income. However, they tended to depress wages for American farm workers.

It is uncertain whether some of the large farms in these fruit and vegetable regions would be able to operate if they had to pay the high American standard wage rate. The federal minimum-wage law does not cover farm workers, nor do most state minimum-wage laws cover this group.

In the general farming areas of the northern states, farmers have to compete with factories and other businesses for labor, so that even without a minimum-wage law, farm wages have held at a fairly high level during the post-World War II years. This has been an important factor in increasing the speed of mechanization and other technological improvements. It has paid farmers to substitute capital for labor.

Though there are exceptions, the general conclusion must be that technical advances in agriculture have not compelled a change in farm organization.

On this, as on so many other things, Karl Marx was wrong. Marx, a city man who knew little about farming, observed the effects of the industrial revolution in increasing the size of factories and business organizations. Manufacturing shifted from family enterprises to large firms with battalions of workers to run the new machines. He con-cluded that the same development was inevitable in agriculture. Com-munist countries have been trying dogmatically to impose the factory system on agriculture ever since—with a striking record of failure.

Strangely, capitalist industrialists often jump to the same conclu-sion Marx reached. They believe the corporate form of organization, with large-scale business units, would be more efficient for farming. They believe the "production line" system could be applied in agricul-ture.

But so far, at least, the industrial revolution in agriculture, which has reached its highest level in the United States, has not produced this result. A research economist for the U.S. Department of Agricul-ture, after a study of farm organization trends, reached this conclusion in a report published January 1962: "The findings of this report lend no support to the popular impression that farm technological advance (especially mechanization) of the kind thus far experienced is incom-patible with an agriculture composed predominantly of family-operated farms."

One reason may be that the family farm is a deeply rooted Amer-ican ideal and has been favored in law and custom throughout United States history. But there have been no significant restraints on the growth of large farming businesses, employing large numbers of hired workers. A good many such firms always have existed along with the predominant family farms. The American way is not to establish rigid forms of economic organization by law, the way Communist countries do. The family farm may be idealized in political speeches, poetry, and song. But it has to prove its place on practical grounds of efficiency to stay alive in America.

Marxists and other skeptics may argue that even though most of United States agriculture is organized in family-sized farms, the families living on the farms may be losing control of managerial decisions. This could come about through loss of ownership, for example. Tenancy in itself does not imply an end to independent family farming. Some highly successful farmers choose to rent land and invest their capital in machinery and livestock. So long as they have secure tenure or easy access to alternative land for rent, they can be as independent as a landowning farmer. But perhaps large numbers of farms are coming under the ownership of big landlords or business firms, with the farmers operating the farms under close direction and limited managerial independence.

The facts do not bear this out. Actually the proportion of farms owned by the operators has been increasing since the 1930s and now is at the highest level in history. Farm ownership by the operator declined for half a century up to about 1930 and has been rising since. Nearly 80 per cent of United States farms are owned partly or wholly by the operators. However, only about 55 per cent of the farm land is under owner-operatorship; 35 per cent is under rentership; and 10 per cent under paid management. This is because more of the larger farms are rented or operated for owners by paid managers. Smaller farms tend to be operated by the owners.

Another sign that independently managed family farms were on the decline would be an increase in the number and acreage of farms directed by professional managers. But that has not happened either. The land-tenure pattern has remained almost unchanged since the 1930s.

A third development that would upset the conclusions reached here would be an increase in contract farming, where the farmer merely performs the labor under the direction of a contractor who buys his crop. Conceivably such a trend could destroy family farming. It would deprive operators of primary control over their farm operations. One form of tenancy approaching contract farming is the sharecropping system of the old plantation days in the south. This is almost gone today.

Another style of contract farming, however, has been coming in to American agriculture. We will discuss this development in the next chapter. It is too early to say whether it may some day change the family-farm system of the United States. As of today it clearly has not done so.

12 / AGRI-BUSINESS

THOUGH THE REVOLUTION of farm technology has not changed the organization of farms in the United States, it has profoundly altered the functions of the farmer.

A century ago, farm families produced all their own food (except salt, sugar, spices, and such items) and much of their clothing—spinning and weaving the wool from their own sheep. Farm families produced their own fuel. The farmer developed his own power supply by raising horses. He produced or bought from neighboring farmers his own seeds, feed for livestock, building materials, and nearly everything else he used.

Gradually, as towns and cities grew, specialization increased. A farmer began to hire carpenters, blackmiths, and other craftsmen to perform tasks he had done himself. He sold more of his products for money, and in turn used the money to buy goods for his family consumption and farm production supplies.

The evolution from self-sufficiency to a market economy proceeded slowly over the five decades from the Civil War to World War I. Beginning about 1920 the rate of change speeded up with the introduction of the tractor and the automobile. But the changes in the 1920s and 1930s were a snail's pace compared to the revolution that began during World War II and has continued, with no sign of slowing down, since then.

Hundreds of services and forms of production formerly done on the farm have been moved off the farm. The farmer today buys from nonfarm business not only many of the things he traditionally produced for himself but a host of new supplies, such as the modern weed-killing chemicals, which never existed before.

John H. Davis, a former United States assistant secretary of agriculture, coined the term "agri-business" to cover the whole complex of relationships between farming proper and nonfarm business which serves farming. "The term agri-business," Davis said, "encompasses today roughly the same scope of functions included under the term agriculture before the intrusion of technology."

Considering the scope of the changes in functions on the farm, it is remarkable that the family farm remains the dominant form of organization of the farm firm. The introduction of mechanical power and the revolution in technology have transferred economic functions out of agriculture. But they have not changed the structure. Another way to say this is that technology has changed the *nature* of what we call agriculture but not its form.

The farmer today depends on nonfarm suppliers for power, equipment, repairs; for seed, fertilizer, insect-control chemicals, weed-control materials; for mixed feeds, including antibiotics, growth stimulators, trace mineral elements, and vitamins; for veterinary, soil- and water-engineering, and other techincal services.

It is not just that the farmer buys materials, he often buys the application of them as well. It is common, for example, instead of buying sacks of fertilizer to hire the local farm supply cooperative to spread the fertilizer on the field. Gas and liquid fertilizer are applied with machines which most farmers cannot afford to own. At the same time that the fertilizer is spread, insecticides or pre-emergence weed-killers may be added to the fertilizer and incorporated into the topsoil. For many farmers it is cheaper to hire this work done by the seller of the chemicals than to do it himself, to say nothing of the convenience and assurance of expert work.

Buying of services of this kind is another reason, in addition to labor-saving machinery, why the employment of hired labor on the farm has declined so sharply.

The blend of farm and nonfarm work is so complex that it is becoming more and more difficult to tell what a farm worker is. In 1963 the Department of Agriculture found about 3.6 million persons who did some farm wage work. Of these, 1.1 million also worked in nonfarm jobs for wages part of the time. Between 1960 and 1963 the proportion of persons in farm employment who did not live on farms rose from 25 per cent to 32 per cent.

The total labor force living on farms, including family as well as hired labor, numbered about 5.5 million persons in 1963. Of these, 1.9 million or about 35 per cent were employed in nonagricultural work. The table in Chapter 2 (page 14) shows the high proportion of income from nonfarm sources of families living on farms.

The Department of Agriculture has made estimates of nonfarm income received by farm families for different income classifications of farms. It is surprising to learn that even in the top-income groups, averaging $10,000 family income in 1959, about $2,000 of this came from off-farm sources. In the lower-income groups, as you would expect, the proportions of off-farm income are larger. For the farms in the lowest commercial class, those with sales of from $2,500 to $5,000 per year, almost half the family income is derived from off-farm sources.

It is a fair presumption that much of this off-farm income in strictly rural communities is in the form of wages for work related to agriculture. It might be work done for other farmers, such as putting up and repairing fences, tilling, clearing brush, spreading fertilizer, combining, or corn picking. It might be work for a local farm-supply or machinery dealer.

The specialization of machines for various kinds of field work and for using the new chemicals makes possible the growth of new businesses to serve farming, takes functions away from the farm, takes labor off the farm—but also provides new work for farm people. Instead of each farmer doing everything for himself, he buys and sells services within the farming community. It is reminiscent of the work-sharing of the pioneer days, in building loghouses, putting up the harvest by teamwork, etc., but only vaguely reminiscent. The modern

Des Moines Register and Tribune

work-sharing is strictly a business proposition. It is an integration of business and farming, a growing specialization of farm operations that can be bought and sold.

The modern commercial farmer is a manager who brings together capital, raw materials, labor, and knowledge from many sources to get the production job done on his farm.

A parallel change has occurred in the farm home. The farmer's wife no longer sews all the family clothing. Many farm wives do little canning of vegetables and fruits these days. They buy most of their groceries at the grocery store, like city women. Furthermore, the farm family eats meals out in restaurants a great deal more than in an earlier time. The farm family usually maintains a vegetable garden, but even this activity has diminished in recent years as agriculture has become more commercial.

The farmer has become a part of the industrial economy. And in

Besides choosing the best hybrid varieties, the farmer takes other measures to produce a vigorous crop. With chemicals he fertilizes the soil, guards against weeds, and regulates the growth of the plants. Left, a farmer sprays his field for corn borers. Right, rotating sprinklers increase the yield in less humid parts of the western corn belt.

Des Moines Register and Tribune

a real and practical sense, he has lost much of his independence. He is dependent on nonfarm industry in order to be able to operate. The self-sufficient entrepreneur able to stand on his own feet and do as he pleases, as Jeffersonian political theory and classical economic theory assumed, cannot exist in a modern economy. In earlier times when prices of farm products declined and the farmer's gross income was reduced, he could reduce many of his cash expenditures, "tighten his belt," and still get along. Today many of his cash expenses are irreducible. He cannot operate without gasoline and oil, for example. So in a period of reduced gross income, the farmer's net income shrinks rapidly.

The rise of new technology in farming has caused an increase in specialization of farming enterprises as well as work functions. As the techniques of farming have become more complex, requiring more specialized knowledge, it has paid farmers to concentrate on the crops or livestock which they can produce most efficiently. Skilled farm management has become more necessary for successful commercial farming. The result has been increasing concentration of dairying on specialized dairy farms, poultry production on specialized poultry farms, and so on.

In the 1920s and 1930s nearly every farm family raised chickens and produced eggs. The eggs would be taken to town by the housewife to trade for the few grocery items bought in those days to supplement home-produced food. Similarly, nearly every farm had milk cows, at least one or two for the family milk and butter supply. Most farm families in the middle west maintained a small dairy herd, because the cream check coming in every month provided a regular cash income. The milk often was separated from the cream, the skim milk fed to pigs, and the cream sold for butter-making.

Nowadays most farmers don't bother with dairy cows and many not with chickens but buy their milk and eggs at the grocery store the same as city people.

Instead of being a jack of all trades, self-reliant and beholden to no man, the modern commercial farmer is a specialized businessman tied up inextricably with suppliers, servicemen, marketing agencies, and the credit system.

Today's average farmer spends about 70 per cent of his gross farm income for the goods, materials, and services he uses in farm production. Gross farm income in the United States in 1963 totaled $41 billion. Of this, farmers spent $29 billion on purchased production supplies and services. If only commercial farms are included, the percentage of gross farm income used for production expenses is even higher.

As was noted earlier, many people have expected that the technical revolution in farming and increasing commercialization would lead to the formation of large-scale "factory farms" with much hired labor. But this has not occurred on a significant scale. Farms have grown in size, to be sure, but continue to be predominantly family farms.

It also has been predicted that the need for good management of highly technical farm operations would result in some form of "integration" of family farms. This might be done through contract farming, where the farmer would produce at the direction of a processor or supplier, for a guaranteed price. Though there are signs of an increase in this sort of arrangement, they are, speaking of agriculture in general, far from a dominant trend.

Contract farming long has been important in vegetable farming. About two-thirds of the vegetables raised for canning and freezing are grown under contract with processors. Vegetables grown for fresh markets are sometimes contracted by dealers from farmers, but more often not.

Practically all fluid milk is produced under contract, usually through a producer's cooperative association. Sugar cane and sugar beets are grown largely under contract with refining companies. Citrus fruits are another example of crops grown under contract with producer cooperatives.

Contract production has developed most rapidly in poultry production in the last dozen years or so. About 95 per cent of the chicken broilers produced in the United States are now grown under some kind of integration or contract scheme. Usually dealers in poultry feed have been the "contractors" or "integrators" of production. They often started by financing farmers in new equipment and feed. In most cases now there is a minimum guarantee to the grower, with adjustments for the amount of weight of broilers produced per unit of feed. Feed, hatching, and processing facilities often have been merged or tied closely together, so that in some parts of the south there are highly integrated "chicken meat-manufacturing" plants.

A similar pattern has developed in turkey production, although the arrangements with feed dealers are more often in terms of conventional lending rather than a true contract.

In the major kinds of livestock, contract production has not amounted to much. Some feed dealers in the middle west have tried hog contracts with a few farmers. The contractor furnishes the feed, the pigs, and general management. He also markets the hogs. The grower is paid a fee per pound of gain in the weight of the hogs.

This system has not been notably successful. The U.S. Department of Agriculture estimates that contract hog production amounts to less than 10 per cent of the total.

Some meat-packing companies and chain stores contract with farmers for feeding beef cattle. Also some cattle ranchers contract with corn-belt farmers to fatten thin range cattle on grain. However, contract cattle feeding remains a relatively unimportant part of the total business.

In Arizona recently the practice of custom feeding of cattle for market has become popular. Operators of large feedlots contract with owners of cattle to fatten them to market quality. A large percentage of the custom-fed cattle is owned by large cattle "operators" who buy thin cattle and then turn them over on contract to a custom-feeding yard for "finishing" to the right degree of fat for slaughter. Some cattle brokers themselves buy bunches of cattle they think are bargains and make deals with custom feeders to make the animals ready for market. Meat-packing companies, ranchers, and even farmers who operate small cattle-feeding businesses may turn cattle over to the custom feedlots for expert feeding.

Businessmen, bankers, lawyers, and other people with money to invest have been attracted to the cattle business in the last 15 years. It has been about the most profitable farming enterprise during this time because of the strong rise in consumer demand for beef. All kinds of business deals have been worked out, including custom feeding by farmers and big commercial feedlots, corporations with their own feeding yards, etc. The decline in cattle prices in 1962-63, because of the huge buildup in cattle production, may have taken some of the enthusiasm out of these investors. Losses in cattle feeding were heavy in 1962, 1963, and 1964.

Studies by Department of Agriculture and state agricultural college research workers continue to show little advantage in cost of production for large-scale cattle-feeding operations as compared with small-farm feedlot operations. Farmers can compete with the big operators on costs because they can utilize feeds that otherwise would have

Recent discoveries in breeding and disease prevention enable modern farmers to raise the healthiest livestock in history. Above, two veterinarians shoot insecticide into the neck of a Hereford.

no market value, as well as labor (their own) not otherwise employable. There is a considerable difference in cost per head, when all operating and fixed costs are figured in, between a cattle-feeding business handling 12,000 head at a time and one handling 100 head or less. However, farm cost studies indicate that most of the economies of scale are achieved by operations as large as 300 to 400 head.

Despite all the talk and experimentation about large-scale "factory" cattle feedlots, the great bulk of the quality beef in this country still is produced by the ordinary, diversified commercial farmer who handles 100 head of cattle a year or fewer.

We can expect further changes in coordination of farm production with marketing and with the suppliers of production materials and services. With continual changes in technology, employing more mechanized techniques, more chemicals, and more capital of all kinds, we also can expect that additional farm production functions will be performed by nonfarm businesses.

This trend is quite visible to farmers and it worries them. They are concerned that increasingly the key decisions affecting agriculture will be made by businesses which sell to farmers or buy from them. They are concerned that integration of production and marketing will go so far that the farmer will be only a hired worker laboring under piecework contracts for those who supply the capital and the expert knowledge. And they fear that the only independent farms which can survive will be those large enough to own all the necessary machines, handle big volumes of livestock and crops, supply their own technical expertise, and manage their own marketing.

The record so far does not justify these fears, but since the farming business is changing so rapidly, under the stress of rapid technical advance, the possibility that "agri-business" may take over cannot be ruled out. The nation's agricultural policies, especially with respect to the incomes of farm families, will largely determine the effect of further technical progress on the structure of the farming business.

13 / PROTECTING FARM INCOME

Because of the farmer's weak bargaining position in an industrial economy, the United States has adopted a number of governmental measures to redress the balance. The United States is not alone in this. Every industrialized country in the world has found it necessary to use the power of government to protect farm income.

Since the 1920s the United States has tried many different ways of supporting prices of farm products above free-market levels, including controlling production of farm products, controlling the distribution of farm products, stimulating the consumption, export, and industrial use of farm products, and establishing "ever normal granary" reserves to stabilize prices.

Some of these government steps have been designed to improve the bargaining power of farmers' private organizations, usually marketing cooperatives. Others have taken the form of direct government action.

In the 1920s federal laws were passed to encourage the cooperative movement in agriculture, and organization of "co-ops" flourished. Farm leaders believed these organizations could provide a solution to the low-income problem by increasing efficiency of the market process and reducing margins between producer and consumer. They also expected to control supplies so as to bargain for higher prices. Working together in cooperatives, it was believed, farmers could gain the market "muscle" they needed to set prices on their produce instead of just taking what was offered.

The cooperatives, however, have been unable to exercise the discipline over marketings and production which could raise gross farm income substantially. They can and do serve as effective means of cutting farm costs—by stimulating competition and establishing a standard for service and a yardstick for prices of farm supplies and of marketing services.

They have developed into a substantial instrument of agricultural marketing and purchasing of farm supplies. In some fields they exercise considerable bargaining power—especially in certain kinds of fruit production. Large proportions of the grain, milk, cotton, tobacco, and fruit production of the United States are handled through cooperatives. Livestock-marketing cooperatives, though important in some areas, have not become a major influence in the sale of livestock.

Farmers' cooperatives have become important in purchasing supplies for farmers. Nearly 10,000 cooperative associations serve farm people, and more than 7,000 of them handle production supplies. About one-fifth of the fertilizer, feed, and petroleum products used by farmers are bought through cooperative associations. In the last several years a number of mergers of cooperatives has taken place, and co-ops have been branching out into many new lines of activity—from ownership of their own oil wells to operation of retail stores.

Cooperatives also are extremely important in the field of electrification. There are about 1,000 rural electric cooperatives. They got their big boost after the establishment of the Rural Electrification Administration (REA) during the presidency of Franklin D. Roosevelt. Before that, private power companies had been reluctant to undertake the investment of providing power for scattered rural families. The REA proved that rural electrification was financially feasible. Today nearly every farm home in the United States obtains electric power from central generating stations.

Farmer cooperatives perform a variety of services for their members, such as spreading fertilizer, grinding and mixing feeds, painting barns and other buildings, testing cows, caring for fruit orchards, repairing farm machinery, developing and maintaining irrigation systems, providing insurance, and performing hundreds of other "agri-business" functions.

But co-ops have been unable to deal with the general problem of overproduction in agriculture.

In the 1920s farmers and their leaders began to realize that the organizing power of the national government was needed to stabilize farm production. A number of proposals were made to Congress for accomplishing this.

The most important of these was a plan to set up a government corporation to buy major farm commodities at a "fair" price. This was to be a price having the same relation to prices of things farmers buy as existed before World War I. The corporation would sell the commodity in the domestic market at this "fair" price and would sell it in the foreign market for whatever it would bring. A two-price system would exist, therefore, for the major farm crops, such as cotton, wheat, corn, and tobacco.

This plan was introduced into Congress by Senator Charles Mc-Nary of Oregon and Representative Gilbert Haugen of Iowa. The McNary-Haugen bills were debated in Congress from 1924 to 1928. The plan was twice passed by Congress and twice vetoed by President Calvin Coolidge.

In the administration of Herbert Hoover, a Federal Farm Board was established to aid farmer cooperatives in their efforts to stabilize prices of farm products. The board was given a fund of $500 million for making loans to coops to enable them to buy up and store farm commodities to stabilize prices.

This operation was a failure. The half-billion-dollar fund was far too small to meet the sudden and drastic decline in world commodity prices in 1930 and 1931.

As a result of this experience farmers, their organizations, and Congress became convinced that production control was needed. In 1933 farm legislation was passed to regulate planting of various crops and to stabilize prices of farm products. An Agricultural Adjustment Administration was established in the U.S. Department of Agriculture

Erosion is most likely to occur if the soil is cultivated up and down the slope. Cultivating across the contour of the land conserves the soil and

in 1933. It had authority to enter into contracts with farmers to limit production of six major products—corn, hogs, wheat, cotton, tobacco, and rice. Processing taxes were collected from processors to pay farmers for cutting production.

In 1936 the Supreme Court struck down this law, declaring the processing tax not a constitutional use of federal taxing power. The Court said the taxes were levied to finance a system of regulating agricultural production, over which Congress had no power.

Congress acted quickly to accomplish the objective in another way. The Court ruled on January 6, 1936. On February 29, 1936, Congress passed the Soil Conservation and Domestic Allotment Act.

[128]

U.S. Department of Agriculture

guards against the disastrous effects, left. Strip cropping—alternating a cultivated row crop with a sod crop—further reduces erosion, right.

This law provided incentive payments to farmers to reduce acreage of basic crops, such as corn, cotton, and wheat, and to shift the land into soil-conserving crops, such as alfalfa and clover. No processing taxes were levied, and the funds came from the federal treasury.

Loans to farmers for storing surplus crops had been provided in the earlier legislation and were not invalidated by the Court. The Commodity Credit Corporation (CCC) was set up for the purpose of handling the loans. This program was a practical method of increasing the farmer's bargaining power. The farmer could hold his crops for a later market instead of having to sell them at harvest time when prices were low. The loans could be paid by turning over the commodity itself to the federal government, so they were in effect a price support or guarantee.

The basic mechanism of farm income support, which was established in the 1930s and has continued ever since, though with modifications, includes these three procedures:

1. Cash payments from the federal treasury to farmers for performing conservation practices.
2. Loans to farmers on crops at a guaranteed price level, constituting a price support.
3. Acreage allotments for farmers to check production of major crops.

The goal for this package of legislation was "parity" prices for farmers, which had become a political slogan in the 1920s. The "fair" price of the McNary-Haugen period now became a precise statistical yardstick or target for New Deal programs. Parity prices were determined for the major farm products. These were the prices which would give a unit of the product (i.e., a bushel of wheat) the same buying power as in the prewar 1910-14 base years for most products. Parity standards have been adjusted several times since then to allow for shifting market-price relationships and changes in costs. The Department of Agriculture still calculates parity prices, and all price-support legislation still is couched in terms of parity. But the big change in the parity concept has been in adjustments of the percentage of parity set as the price support.

As an incentive to production in World War II the standard was raised to 90 per cent of parity. In the 1933-42 period price-support loans were determined at a much lower percentage of full parity, usually from 50 to 75. Ninety per cent of parity continued as the support level for several years after the war, but in 1948 a gradual erosion of this guarantee began, as mounting surpluses accumulated by CCC made it increasingly impractical.

The target of parity has lost much of its early political charm, and the objective of farm legislation more and more has been parity of income. This is not a statistically defined goal (although such a parity income standard was set in law during the New Deal years). Farm policy has become much more educated in the 1960s; it no longer centers on the objective of prices alone.

Over the years the payment, commodity loan, and acreage-control methods have been reinforced by others.

Another price-support technique is the purchase agreement. If the farmer chooses, he can make a purchase agreement with CCC for a stipulated quantity of corn, for example, instead of obtaining a loan. CCC agrees to buy the corn at the price-support level later in the marketing year. The loan suits the needs of producers who require the money immediately and who can meet the storage requirements (bin or corncrib or warehouse with adequate protection against weather,

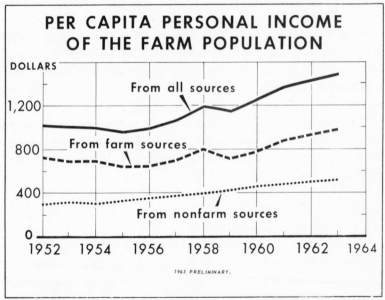

PER CAPITA PERSONAL INCOME
OF THE FARM POPULATION

From all sources

From farm sources

From nonfarm sources

1963 PRELIMINARY.

Economic Research Service, U.S. Department of Agriculture

Even though they lag behind industrial earnings, farm incomes have gone up in recent years. But the principal gains have been from nonfarm sources.

rats, etc.). The purchase agreement furnishes price insurance for the producer who does not need the cash immediately or who cannot meet the storage requirements.

Whether a farmer obtains a loan or makes a purchase agreement, he is assured of the guaranteed price. He must, of course, deliver the required quantity of the specified quality of the commodity in order to get the full amount of the loan or agreement. If the market price rises above the guarantee level, he of course will sell the commodity and pay off his loan or cancel the purchase agreement.

Private lending agencies, mostly local banks, make most of the commodity loans. CCC agrees to take over the loans if requested.

CCC also has been authorized to buy farm commodities directly in the market to support prices. Price support for dairy products and other perishable commodities has been accomplished mostly by direct purchase. CCC buys butter, cheese, and dried milk from manufacturers and handlers of dairy products. This enables these agencies to pay farmers the support price for manufacturing milk and butterfat. Thus farmers do not deal directly with the government. CCC buys directly from producers to some extent, however, in supporting prices of cottonseed and flaxseed.

The secretary of agriculture has power to buy farm commodities for price-support purposes or for market stabilization even when a specified level of price guarantee has not been set. In recent years CCC has bought pork and beef, for example, to buttress declining markets for hogs and cattle. In 1964 large quantities of high-quality beef were bought from meat packers to stabilize prices of fat cattle which had fallen sharply in the previous year.

Unfavorable experience with direct purchase and storage of perishable commodities tends to restrain the secretary of agriculture in using this method. Scandals about spoilage and waste of eggs and potatoes in the late 1940s resulted in the removal of price-support guarantees for these commodities. Succeeding agricultural administrations have been wary of getting caught in similar blasts of unfavorable publicity.

Purchases of meat, poultry, butter, and other perishables are quickly disposed of through the various avenues of food distribution open to the government, including direct distribution through local relief agencies, the school-lunch program, and public institutions.

The federal government also helps producers of certain commodities improve their bargaining power by means of federal market orders and agreements. These programs do not involve the government in buying, selling and storing commodities. They are devices to establish orderly marketing conditions. Market orders enable dairymen in a city "milk shed," usually organized in a cooperative, to bargain more effectively with distributors and to fix prices for their milk. A market order issued by the secretary of agriculture is binding on all handlers of the commodity within a specified production area. Under milk market orders, the producer cooperatives can control the supply going into fluid (fresh) milk distribution. The surplus is usually processed into manufactured products for which the return to the dairyman is lower. Thus the market order, in effect, enables the producers through their marketing cooperative to maintain a two-price system for milk and to exercise a degree of control over production.

Market orders for milk are not accompanied by marketing agreements. But most market-order programs for other commodities do not establish minimum prices and instead seek to enhance prices through marketing agreements. Fruits, vegetables, tree nuts, and other commodities are covered by such agreements. They provide for regulations on grade, size, quality, maturity, quantity eligible for marketing, and the diversion of surpluses into lower uses. For example, the best qualities of navel oranges go into sale as fresh fruit, while lower grades are used for processing. Some agreements provide for the establishment of reserve pools for control and distribution of surpluses. Agreements may also prohibit unfair trade practices and provide for market expansion, research, development, and other programs.

Special subsidies to producers of certain commodities have been paid at various times. During World War II subsidies were paid to beef-cattle feeders, for example, in order to maintain their returns without increasing prices to consumers. This is the form of subsidy paid to producers of most farm commodities in England.

It has been advocated off and on in the United States as a method of protecting the returns of producers of perishable commodities but has not won acceptance for peacetime. The idea is to allow market prices to seek their own level but to pay producers the difference between the market level and the guaranteed "fair" price. This avoids the problems of storage and disposal of products which deteriorate in storage. It also is a good way of keeping prices down for consumers if it is deemed advisable to do so at the expense of taxpayers. This is the main reason for the direct-payment policy in England. High incentives to farmers are provided by the subsidies, but retail prices are held to a modest level. This shifts food costs slightly from low-income families who pay little or no income taxes to income taxpayers, in line with the graduated scale of the income tax.

The cost of such a program could be astronomical if there were no method of holding production in check. One of the principal reasons direct payments based on a price-support guarantee have not been politically acceptable in the United States is the fear that government costs would skyrocket. In England costs can be kept in line by control of imports. Since the United Kingdom imports a third or more of its food supply, market prices can be raised or lowered by adjusting the volume of imports.

The only two direct-payment programs based on price guarantees in this country are for commodities which the United States imports heavily (the major part of its supplies of these commodities). These are the subsidies for wool producers and sugar growers.

A wool producer sells his wool in normal marketing channels. At the end of the year he receives a government payment covering the difference between the average price received by wool producers during the year and the previously announced support price. The same return could be provided for American wool growers by raising the tariff on wool and thus lifting the entire wool price level for consumers. The subsidy, as an alternative to the higher import duty, encourages larger wool production in this country than could be maintained in open competition with the efficient wool producers of Australia and New Zealand.

The same is true for the sugar subsidy. Sugar is the one farm commodity in the United States that is completely managed by the federal government. In December of each year the secretary of agriculture estimates the sugar requirements of the nation for the following year. Under the Sugar Act of 1948, quotas of this supply are assigned to domestic and foreign producing areas. A tax of 50 cents per hundredweight on all domestic and foreign sugar covers the costs of the subsidies to domestic producers. In this case, therefore, the subsidy is paid by Americans as consumers of sugar, rather than as taxpayers.

The purpose of the government programs for sugar and wool producers is to protect them against foreign competition and to maintain larger domestic production of these commodities than would exist without subsidies. The price and income protection programs for other farm producers are quite the reverse. They are designed to protect farmers against their own surplus production, to prevent abundance from being a curse to those who create it.

Fundamentally this policy rests on the commodity price-support system for major crops, backed up by acreage limitations and payments for land retirement or conservation practices. Since the original legislation was passed in the 1930s, the acreage controls for wheat, cotton, tobacco, and rice have been strengthened. If two-thirds of the producers of these commodities approve, "marketing quotas" may be applied. "Marketing quota" is a misnomer, for producers are required only to keep their plantings of the commodity within their acreage allotments. If they grow more than the allotted acreage and sell the crop, they are subject to penalties. But there are no quotas in pounds or bushels, and a farmer may sell legally all he can produce on his allotted acreage.

Legislation passed during the 1950s pioneered a new kind of crop-acreage-reduction scheme, a plan for "retiring" cropland on a long-term basis. In effect, the farmer rents some of his land to the federal government, agreeing not to harvest a crop or to pasture livestock on the land. In return he receives a payment from the government. This program, called the Soil Bank (or Conservation Reserve), was discontinued in 1961, though some of the land retired will remain out of production for several years and a small portion of it which was planted to trees probably will be permanently converted from crop production. It seems likely that a new long-range cropland retirement or "conversion" program will be enacted, however, since the necessity of reducing total land in grain crops is the one farm policy upon which all the farm organizations and both political parties agree.

This general program of acreage control, price support, and storage for the major crops provides a shelter for all of American agriculture. It is true that growers of many commodities are not themselves troubled with visible surpluses. The excess production capacity shows up largely in grain, both food grain (wheat) and feed grain (largely corn). About 90 per cent of all United States land in crops, hay, and pasture is used for either food grain or feed for livestock. Thus the grain-livestock sector is dominant in United States farming.

Since nearly every farmer can grow grain and hay or grass for pasturage, and produce livestock, this big sector of farming tends to be a shock-absorber for all the rest. If cotton or tobacco farmers must cut output to balance markets, they turn to grain or other feed crops and compete with livestock producers.

So when people say that the farm surplus is only in grain and that many other commodities are in balance with markets, they are voicing an illusion. Some critics of farm programs have declared that 75 per cent of agriculture is not affected by government programs—and is doing well. They are referring to the fact that prices of most crops and livestock (those accounting for 75 per cent of total farm income) are not directly supported by the government. But if acreage restrictions and price supports for wheat and other grains were to be abandoned, the surplus would spill over into these other commodities.

Grain is raw material for livestock production. By restricting grain

U.S. Department of Agriculture

Agricultural advances are meaningless unless they are adopted on the farm. For more than a hundred years, the Department of Agriculture has operated a far-reaching educational program. Through meetings, clubs, schools, colleges, publications, radio programs, and trained extension workers, many farmers have adapted to the change from farming by hand to farming by machine. In this photo, taken in 1920, a youth camp instructor explains how a gasoline engine operates.

output and use (that is, by storing surplus stocks) and supporting grain prices, the program also restrains livestock production and supports livestock prices.

The sheltering effect of the grain-acreage-reduction, price-support, and storage and disposal programs is not well understood even among farmers themselves. Western cattlemen, for example, pride themselves on being independent of government; they regularly pass resolutions at their association meetings calling for an end to government interference,* an end to price supports, and so on. But the facts show plainly that among the largest beneficiaries of the government grain programs have been the beef-cattle raisers. An acre of grain produces many more pounds of beef than an acre of grass, especially when you are comparing an acre of Iowa corn land with an acre of Wyoming range. If there were no restraints on corn acreage, and if corn prices dropped to 75 cents a bushel, as they probably would with full output and no price support, beef, pork and poultry-meat production would rise tremendously. Cattle and hog prices would be cut by half or more.

Western cattlemen evidently think that curbs on corn production, which reduce the demand of midwestern farmers for range cattle for feeding, are harmful to their interests. What they forget is that this reduces meat output and thus supports livestock prices. A similar short-sightedness has been shown by dairy and poultry producers, who object to grain programs that raise their feed costs. Yet cheap feed always increases total production of competitive high-protein foods (meat, milk, and eggs) thus lowering net returns for all livestock producers.

A number of independent studies by agricultural economists at state agricultural colleges and at the U.S. Department of Agriculture in recent years have reached remarkably similar conclusions as to the effect of the grain programs. If these programs alone were discontinued for a period of five years, while others were continued, the researchers found, the net income of farmers from sales of farm products would decline from 19 to 40 per cent. The average of the estimates would indicate a drop of one-third in farm income.

One of the most recent studies of the effect of supply control programs is an analysis of excess capacity in American agriculture by Luther G. Tweeten and Fred H. Tyner, of Oklahoma State Univer-

---

* This seems not to be a matter of principle, since these same cattlemen clamored for government protection against beef imports when cattle prices fell in 1963.

sity.* Tweeten and Tyner found that in the 1958-63 period, assuming no acreage and commodity-diversion programs, farmers would have attempted to market 7 per cent more products than could be moved through market channels at the prevailing prices of those years. They concluded that prices of farm products would have to decline about 20 per cent to permit farm output to clear the market.

Such a drop in prices received by farmers would reduce net farm income by more than 50 per cent because of the high level of fixed costs of farm production. A depression of farm income of this size probably would curtail expenditures for fertilizer and some other production supplies which could be postponed. This would reduce farm production within a few years, resulting in some recovery of prices of farm products. In making their estimates of the effects of a return to the free market in agriculture, the economists allowed for a reduction in crop yields. They assumed that the farm programs had been discontinued for three to five years.

Even after this much adjustment to free market conditions had occurred, farm income would still be reduced to about half the 1963-64 level of around $12.5 billion per year. In a longer time, however, enough farmers would be driven out of business to bring about a greater cut in production and a rise in income. But it would take a considerable length of time.

It is this inability of agriculture to adjust its output without adjusting its production capacity that causes all the trouble. Without government help, agriculture cannot regulate output by utilizing capacity more or less fully, the way most other industries do. Agriculture cannot adapt itself to technological advance or to changes in demand without government programs.

Governmental attempts to provide equality of income opportunities for farm people involve collective restraints on individual action. Such restraints are distasteful to many people. They are incompatible

---

* "Excess Capacity in U.S. Agriculture," *Agricultural Economics Research* (U.S. Department of Agriculture, January 1964).

with fundamental beliefs about freedom of enterprise. Thus there is a continuing political struggle within agriculture about production and marketing "controls."

Consequently the so-called controls never have been very severe. In the years of the Great Depression, when the government programs began, farmers were willing to accept more restraints than they will accept now. It was assumed then that these restraints were temporary, as a means of warding off severe decline in farm income as a result of the depression. It was believed that when unemployment was ended and business recovery came, farm controls could be abandoned.

Since the 1950s, however, the chronic nature of the overproduction situation in agriculture has become more apparent. It is now widely realized that agriculture needs long-range machinery to balance supply with demand if farm people are to have equal earning opportunities with people in other occupations.

One of the appealing suggestions which pops up from time to time is that agriculture may be able to *sell* its way out of trouble by getting people to eat more luxury foods. It is often said that if consumers could be persuaded to spend just a bit more money for meat and dairy products instead of automobiles, for example, this would solve the farm problem.

It is also said that if consumption of meat, milk, and eggs could be increased substantially, the surplus would disappear. Livestock condense five to seven pounds of dry matter in the form of grain and other feed to about one pound of dry matter in the form of livestock products. So it would take more acres and more capital and labor to provide an animal diet than a grain or cereal diet.

Switching consumer buying toward more livestock products seems a good possibility when you look at the amount of meat consumed in Uruguay, Australia, and New Zealand. These countries consume much more meat per person than we do in the United States. Their average meat consumption is around 220 or 230 pounds per person per year. In the United States it is around 160 pounds. The trend of consumption in the United States has been toward more meat and other livestock products and less cereals and potatoes. So why not promote meat heavily and speed up this trend?

People who advocate such a program often forget how much promotion and advertising is being carried on now. It is estimated that about 2 billion dollars, one-fifth of all the money spent on advertising in this country, is directed toward promotion of food products. A large share of this is for animal products. The meat packers and dairy companies are heavy advertisers, as are retail grocers. In addition, the National Livestock and Meat Board promotes meat products, and a large number of other public and private agencies are pushing the consumption of meat.

Thus the real question is whether *additional* large expenditures for advertising livestock products would accomplish much. In recent years there has been a large expansion in such activity, and there is no evidence that this has had a marked effect on demand for meat.

Many farmers and farm organizations seem to gather a psychic return out of an advertising program, because they feel they are doing something to help themselves and not calling on the government for assistance. Maybe this psychic return is sufficient to justify additional advertising expenditures, with the money raised from farmers by means of a check-off deduction from livestock sales.

But farmers should not count on such a program to correct the oversupply situation in general. It may be possible for the producers of a specialty product to benefit greatly from advertising. But this only increases the consumption of that product at the expense of some other—there is no net gain for agriculture as a whole.

Another solution often proposed is similar to the promotion and advertising idea. This is *to improve the quality of a product* and thus get the consumer to spend more money for it.

A great deal of effort has been expended in recent years on encouraging the meat-type hog. Many have believed that pork consumption has lost ground in comparison with beef and poultry because consumers are shunning fats. If consumption of pork had increased in the same proportion as beef and poultry in the last 30 years, we might not have a grain-surplus problem—at least it would be far less troublesome.

The experience of Canada is instructive on this point. The Canadians have been energetically improving the quality of their pork for a good many years. The Canadian government has a strict grading program, with government employees grading carcasses as they hang on the rail in the meat cooler. Government premiums are paid for top quality carcasses. Canadian hog production today is practically all of the lean, meat-type animals. If there are good possibilities for expanding the demand for pork in this way, we certainly should expect it to show up strongly in the Canadian experience.

But it does not. The hog industry has lost just as much ground in Canada as in the United States in the last 30 years.

Pork consumption in the late 1920s and early 1930s in the United States was around 46 per cent of the total consumption of all meat and poultry. In recent years this figure has declined to about 34 per cent. In Canada in the 1920s and 1930s pork consumption was about 43 per cent of the total of meat and poultry, but it has now declined to about 30 per cent.

The evidence is clear that the Canadian pork producer, despite his quality-improvement program, has lost in the competitive battle with other meat producers just as the United States pork producer has lost.

So it would appear that there is no easy solution to the surplus problem by improving quality of pork. The evidence in Canada isn't very promising even for pork to hold its own in the battle with other meats by quality improvement. The reasons for the consumer preference for beef and poultry are not clear. But apparently it is not entirely a matter of the fat in pork, or the experience in Canada would be different from our own.

A third method of curing the farm problem which has many adherents is collective bargaining. The idea here is to get farmers to cooperate in withholding their products from the market, thus forcing processors to pay a higher price. A statement by the National Catholic

Rural Life Conference, for example, said, "We urge farmers, in so far as it is possible, to keep their produce until those who wish to buy are willing to bargain with them in good faith. Prices should be determined, not by the supply which happens to reach the market at a given time, but by a contract established by the farmers' cooperative organization with processors, wholesalers, etc."

The National Farmers Organization has built up a large membership on this collective bargaining idea. It is a fact that individual farmers lack bargaining power. They can accomplish useful results through cooperative marketing organizations. Collective bargaining undoubtedly can be beneficial. It has *proved* to be beneficial, in the case of specialty fruit, nut, and vegetable crops. Here you have a relatively small number of growers in a localized area, dealing with a cannery or one or two outlets, perhaps. Also cooperative bargaining organizations can help in cases of seasonal surplus. Such organizations can carry on diversion programs, which means selling the surplus at a lower price for a lower use—such as potatoes used for starch manufacturing.

However, it is a long jump from this kind of collective bargaining to collective bargaining for a commodity such as hogs, beef cattle, corn, or wheat—commodities produced by a million or more farmers nationwide. The collective bargainers are kidding themselves if they think they can bargain their way to higher prices on commodities of this kind—*unless they can limit production.*

You have no real bargaining power on hogs, for example, unless you're willing actually to reduce the supply. Just holding hogs off the market for a few weeks would not yield much bargaining power. In fact the total supply of pork would be larger as a result of keeping the animals on the farm and fattening them to heavier weight. And prices would be lower. Those who want to institute collective bargaining on hog prices will have to find some way of not merely holding the hogs for two weeks, but limiting their farrowings in the first place, or being prepared to kill some of the little pigs without feeding them out to maturity for pork production.

A fourth favorite solution is to expand the demand for food by government action—*providing food for the needy* overseas and at home. We often hear people say there is no farm surplus so long as there are hungry people.

University of Minnesota farm economists carried on an extensive study of the possibilities of increasing the consumption of food in the United States by government programs. They found that if every person now undernourished were given an adequate diet, this would increase the expenditures for food only 1 or 2 per cent. The fact is that most people in America are well fed. Some might eat a few more steaks and chops, a higher *quality* diet, but there are no *large* gains to be made here—even if the government were to subsidize a good diet for all those who cannot afford it.

So far as the poor people of the world are concerned, the opportunities would seem unlimited. However, there are many practical difficulties. Other exporting countries object to our giving away food which may hurt their markets. In some countries transportation and distribution systems cannot handle a large volume of imported food. In many places the local farmers resent competition from the United States government. Governments do not want to accept large grants of food unless they know these will continue for some time ahead. And all countries want to develop their own food-producing capacity.

This is not to argue against Food for Peace or food for the hungry here at home. It is only a word of caution on expecting these efforts to solve the surplus problem.

Outlets for food could be expanded, perhaps, if the emphasis were shifted more from "disposal" to "human welfare." If we decided to furnish better-balanced rations for Pakistan and India, instead of sending mainly those products technically in surplus, we might do a far better job for the Indians and Pakistanis, and we might provide an outlet for many more acres of United States crops.

The same is true of domestic food programs. But after doing all that can be done to assure that our food is used to improve human well-being here and abroad, we are still likely to have a considerable oversupply.

When farmers decide that they are ready to work together to limit their output to keep it in line with markets at a reasonable price, the job can be done. There are not many signs that farmers are willing to do this now, or that the public would tolerate government regimentation of agriculture to achieve it.

The alternative method of keeping farm incomes up, *direct subsidies* from the government, probably would not be very acceptable to farmers. It would not be popular with the taxpayers who think federal farm programs are too costly the way they are.

14 / FARM SUBSIDIES,
COSTS, AND BENEFITS

A N ANALYST for a large commodity and security brokerage house was quoted as follows in *Barron's* financial weekly in March 1963:

> The farm program, since its inception, has cost some $100 billion . . . . Counting compound interest on these out payments, the cost easily exceeds half of the national debt. We spend $5 billion interest a year on . . . debt . . . caused by the farm program, and have expended an average of $7 billion in recent years for program costs. Thus we are paying $12 billion a year for past and present farm programs . . . .

Such remarks using similar absurd calculations are not uncommon. The high cost of "farm subsidies" has been a political target for many years. Usually, as in the above example, the critics assume that the entire expenditures of the U.S. Department of Agriculture are subsidies for farm people.

It is true that the Department of Agriculture budget has been averaging nearly $7 billion a year in the 1950s and 1960s, but that's the only thing true about the above statement. The $7 billion seems outrageous when you compare it with the number of farms, which has been declining rapidly. In the 1959 census of agriculture there were 3.7 million farms in the United States. Divide that into $7 billion and you get nearly $2,000 of federal expenditure per farm. If the 1.6 million farms with sales less than $2,500 per year are eliminated as "noncommercial," that leaves only about 2 million *real* farms. Most of the 1.6

million noncommercial farms are part-time, residential, or subsistence farms. Now divide the 2 million commercial farms into the $7 billion. It appears that Uncle Sam is spending an average of $3,500 for each real farm in the country.

What such comparisons do not show is that a large share of government spending through the Department of Agriculture is for general public purposes rather than for agricultural subsidies. The accompanying table (page 150) shows a breakdown of the Department of Agriculture budgets for fiscal years 1964 and 1965. The figures are broadly representative of the entire 1955-64 period.

Federal programs to supply food as foreign aid to other countries obviously should not be charged entirely as a subsidy to agriculture. Exports of food at cutrate prices and donations of food to other countries do benefit agriculture, of course. They remove supplies of grain and other products from United States markets and thus ease the surplus problem.

However, foreign aid in money also benefits certain United States industries. If a country is given a grant of $50 million which it spends for industrial machinery in the United States, should this be labeled in the federal budget as a subsidy to the machine-tool industry? The Food for Peace program is part of the national foreign aid effort and logically should be classed as foreign aid the same as other grants or loans to foreign countries.

Money spent for distribution of food to people in public institutions, people on public welfare programs, and schoolchildren benefits farmers. It is doubtful that farmers receive a direct increase in income from these food distribution programs, but the programs may help to educate some people to eat better diets and thus ultimately increase spending for food. Studies by the Department of Agriculture indicate that the total demand for farm products in the country is increased only very slightly by such programs. The main benefit is to the recipients of the food.

One of the biggest illusions in "farm subsidy" accounting is to classify the agricultural research, education, and technical assistance programs as subsidies to the farmer.

These public efforts, as was pointed out in previous chapters, stimulate more efficient farm production and help the consumer directly by lowering the cost of food. It is true that individual farmers who are first to adopt new methods gain a temporary benefit from improved efficiency. But as soon as the majority of farmers adopt those methods, the gain is lost. In fact farmers collectively lose from this public investment in increased production, because a larger supply sells for less money.

If farm technology had been frozen at the 1940 level, farm income would be much higher today than it actually is. Even if there had been no reduction in the farm population since 1940, the per-capita income of farm people would be much higher today, if there had been no change in farming technology since then. The reason is that production would have failed to advance as rapidly as demand for food. Prices of farm products would be far higher and net farm incomes much larger.

The government investment in better farm methods has paid off many times over to the public and should be charged as a public benefit rather than as a subsidy to agriculture.

The rapid introduction of new technology into agriculture is the primary cause of the surplus problem. It is the reason why production controls, price supports, and other subsidies are necessary. In a sense, the expenditures in the lower half of the table (page 151) are a consequence of the expenditures for research and education just above them. If the government spent money only for research and education in agriculture, the farmer's income would slide downhill rapidly.

The cost of government farm programs to support prices and improve incomes of farmers has been much less than the gain to consumers from improvements in farm productivity. Economist Walter Wilcox, of the Library of Congress, calculated that food costs in 1963 were $4 billion to $6 billion less than they would have been if prices

U.S. Department of Agriculture Budget Expenditures
Fiscal Years 1964 and 1965 (Based on 1965 Midyear Budget Review)

	1964 [a]	ESTIMATED 1965
	(MILLIONS)	

PROGRAMS WHICH BENEFIT THE GENERAL PUBLIC:

Programs having foreign relations and defense aspects:

	1964 [a]	1965
Sales of surplus agricultural commodities for foreign currencies	$1,452	$1,301
Emergency famine relief to friendly peoples	215	244
Donations of commodities acquired by Commodity Credit Corporation (CCC)	345	298
International Wheat Agreement	86	20
Transfer of bartered materials to supplemental stockpile	83	89
Long-term supply contracts	53	183
Payments to Veterans Administration and armed services for milk and other dairy products used in excess of normal requirements	45	41
Total	2,279	2,176

Food distribution programs:

Purchases of surplus agricultural commodities	236	239
Commodities acquired by CCC	246	179
Pilot food stamp plan	30	51
School lunch program	180	193
Special milk program	97	100
Total	789	762

Investment in Rural Electrification Administration (REA) and Farmers Home Administration (FHA) loans, which are subject to repayment:

REA loans	330	383
FHA loans	220	219
Total	550	602

Long-range programs for the improvement of agricultural resources, including research, meat inspection, disease and pest control, education, market development and services, protection of soil and water resources, and forest and public land management:

Forest Service	315	321
Agricultural Research Service	197	199

[a] Subject to revision when final Treasury figures are available.

	1964 [a]	ESTIMATED 1965
	(MILLIONS)	
Soil Conservation Service	193	198
Extension Service	79	78
Cooperative State Research Service	41	43
Agricultural Marketing Service, marketing services	38	44
Farmers Home Administration, salaries and expenses	38	44
Expenses for other agencies and staff offices	89	98
Total	990	1,025
Total	4,608	4,565

PROGRAMS PRIMARILY FOR STABILIZATION OF FARM INCOME:

	1964	1965
Agricultural conservation program	217	225
Conservation reserve program	290	200
Cropland conversion program	7	10
CCC price-support, supply, and related programs	1,244	−192
Acreage diversion payments:		
Feed grains	646	876
Wheat	115	34
Price-support payments:		
Feed grains	382	374
Wheat	79	—
Cotton equalization payments	63	561
Wheat Marketing Certificate program	—	−108
National Wool Act program	73	39
Agricultural Stabilization and Conservation Service expenses	115	114
Total	3,231	2,133
Sugar Act program	87	88
Total	3,318	2,221
GRAND TOTAL	7,926	6,786

Source: U.S. Department of Agriculture.

of farm products had risen as much as prices in other parts of the economy in the preceding eight years. This amounts to a saving of about $100 per year per American family.

Farm income support programs in recent years have been costing $2 billion to $3 billion per year. In 1953-54 the average cost of these programs was $1.9 billion, and in 1961-62 the average cost was $2.6 billion. The increase in farm subsidy cost to taxpayers during the eight years was about one-seventh the savings in food cost to consumers from improved agricultural efficiency.

For the 27 years from 1933 through 1959 the realized cost of federal programs primarily for the support of prices of farm products totaled about $18 billion. This is an average of $660 million per year. One reason the average cost is so low is that surpluses accumulated in the prewar years were a valuable asset to the government in World War II. Almost the entire cost of prewar farm subsidies was recovered. Surpluses were accumulated during years of big crops and low prices and were put back onto the market during years of short supply and high prices.

If the large quantities of farm products which have been provided to other countries as aid for their development programs were counted as an offset to the cost of price support programs, the net cost of farm subsidies would look even smaller.

Precision in accounting is not possible in such matters. The food-distribution programs and the Food for Peace program should be considered at least in part "farm subsidy." It is evident that United States foreign aid would not have been as large in the 1950s and early 1960s if the surplus farm products had not been on hand ready for use. Also, food-distribution programs at home help to relieve surpluses and add something to total food consumption.

Two conclusions emerge from this analysis: On the whole the expenditures for the U.S. Department of Agriculture have been a wise expenditure from the public viewpoint. And the nature of the accounting system gives a false picture of costs and benefits. It should be changed. Perhaps it would help to rename the Department of Agricul-

U.S. Department of Agriculture

Adjusting to rapid changes has been a major problem for the farmer who was brought up in the old ways of doing things. Schools, colleges, and neighborhood instruction have helped him keep up to date. Above, a soil conservation worker plans a new watershed project with a group of farmers in Gage County, Nebraska.

ture the Department of *Food* and Agriculture. Certainly the American taxpayer-consumer ought to understand that most of the work of his department is in his behalf, rather than in the behalf of the farmer. The intent of the expenditures in nearly all cases is to benefit farmers, to be sure, but the effects of the expenditures are something else again.

The net effect of the total public spending, subsidies to farmers included, has been to increase the quality and quantity of food and to transfer people out of farming at a rapid rate, making them available for other productive work. The taxpayer and consumer have little ground for complaint.

Critics of farm subsidies have a far more reasonable argument when they point out that most of the true farm-subsidy expenditures have gone for the benefit of commercial agriculture. The low-income families in agriculture have received little help from the price-support programs, while many well-to-do families have gained considerably.

The price and income supports are farm *business* programs; that is, they are aimed at the market problems of oversupply, low prices, and the cost-price squeeze. They have not pretended to be welfare programs. Consequently the benefits of these programs accrue to farmers in accordance with the size of their businesses. Though certain advantages have been provided for the smaller family farms as compared with the larger ones, notably through the Farmers Home Administration, and ritual bows are made to the family-farm ideal in all legislation, the impact of the commodity programs tends to be directly related to the amount of the commodity produced. (This impact has not, however, weakened the family-farm structure, though it is growing in average size [see chapter 11].)

Proposals frequently are made to set a maximum of payments under commodity programs or to limit the amount of production eligible for price support. But Congress has shown no disposition (through the year 1964, at least) to accept these limits. The argument that this would place a "ceiling on opportunity" always has been effective. Moreover programs aimed at controlling total output logically should be attractive to the big producers.

Since the largest farm operators receive the largest benefits from income-support programs, it follows that they would suffer most if the supports were removed. A study made for the Senate Committee on Agriculture indicated that if price supports were eliminated, many of the 100,000 farms with annual sales above $40,000 would experience substantial losses.* "For the group as a whole," said the report, "ex-

---

* "Farm Program Benefits and Costs in Recent Years," Committee Print, prepared by Legislative Reference Service, Library of Congress.

penses would exceed income." This is because of the high ratio of cash expense to income on these large farms.

So long as the farm commodity control and price support activities are voluntary, there is no escape from the regressive welfare incidence of the benefits. If the bigger farms were excluded from all participation, the production restraints would be less effective and the public costs for payments and/or price supports would be higher. Cutting off the few very largest farms from full payments might be politically popular. But it should be remembered that a large part of the income gains from the commodity programs are derived through the market. Farmers who are ineligible for corn loans or corn-acreage-diversion payments realize gains through the general market support for feed grain prices. Livestock producers gain through the indirect limitation of livestock output (see page 143). So reducing payments to the "big boys" probably would not result in greater equality in size of farm or help the little fellow.

If subsidies to agriculture were divorced from the market and paid in cash, they could be allocated on a welfare basis or on a basis which would promote greater equality within agriculture. But to maintain farm income at its present level by straight cash payments would be exorbitantly expensive. And it would tend to discourage improvements in production efficiency.

Farm programs designed to keep commercial agriculture healthy, to keep food costs low, and to stimulate technical advance are poorly designed to meet the problems of poverty in agriculture.

15 / POVERTY IN AGRICULTURE

IT IS AMUSING that many of those who object to commercial farm subsidies because these subsidies don't help poor farmers are the same people who oppose welfare programs in general. Critics who blanch at the idea of government action to equalize income, even attacking the progressive income tax for being a drag on incentives, oppose farm supports distributed the way the market distributes income.

About 1.6 million farms, as of the 1959 census, had sales of less than $2,500 that year, which means net cash income less than half that figure. These farms obviously are not in a position to benefit greatly from the programs that raise prices of farm products. They are relatively noncommercial farms. Many of them are residential or part-time farms. But perhaps a million are simply inadequate farms which are the main source of income of the people living on them.

This lower half of agriculture is a blight in America. It is a genuine problem of underdevelopment. Some of the worst slum conditions in the United States exist in rural areas of the southern states and in spots all through the country including the cutover regions of the lake states, the southern fringe of the corn belt, and elsewhere.

The incidence of poverty is much greater in rural than in urban areas. President Johnson has taken $3,000 cash income per year as the dividing line below which families are considered to be in a state of poverty in the middle 1960s. For individuals living alone, $1,500 is the figure. According to the Economic Report of the President, January 1964, more than 40 per cent of all farm families fall below the poverty line (and more than 80 per cent of the nonwhite farm families). More than half the poverty in agriculture exists in the southern states. Nearly 40 per cent is in the north-central states. Here are the numbers of farm families with less than $3,000 cash income in 1959 (from 1960 census):

Total U.S.	1,570,000
South	830,000
North-central	581,000
West	87,000
Northeast	72,000

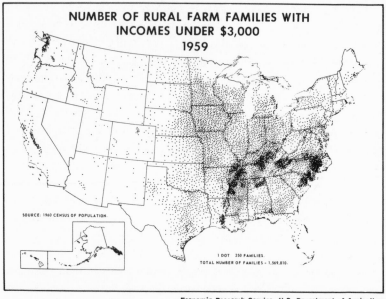

NUMBER OF RURAL FARM FAMILIES WITH INCOMES UNDER $3,000 1959

SOURCE: 1960 CENSUS OF POPULATION.

1 DOT 250 FAMILIES.
TOTAL NUMBER OF FAMILIES - 1,569,810.

Economic Research Service, U.S. Department of Agriculture

For his War on Poverty, President Johnson has taken $3,000 as the minimum family income that is adequate for living in the middle 1960s. More than 40 percent of all farm families fall below the poverty line, and more than half of this 40 percent live in the southern states.

These figures overstate poverty in farming slightly in relation to urban poverty. Farm families receive more nonmoney income in the form of housing and food, which city families generally do not receive.

Income comparisons may overstate farm poverty also because farm families tend to own more property than city families. A survey by the Federal Reserve Board indicated that farm operator families had average net worth of $44,000 in December 1962, compared with $22,600 for all United States families. Farm-operator families do not include wage workers in farming, of course, and all United States families include those on relief and in low-paying jobs, so the figures are not strictly comparable. But they do suggest that the ownership of land and farm capital of farm families offsets to some degree their low incomes in making an assessment of poverty levels.

Elderly people, ready to retire from farming, may be able to sell their farmland, machinery, and livestock, and live on their savings. Even though their income is low, if they have $20,000 or so in savings, they can hardly be classified as poor.

But for a middle-aged farmer, who cannot qualify for nonfarm work, ownership of land and machinery mean little so far as his family's poverty status is concerned. His "wealth" is unrealizable, because he must stay in farming to earn what little income he can. This "boxed-in" individual is the most serious problem of poverty in agriculture.

Government payments and the income-increasing effects of farm programs are distributed roughly the same as cash receipts from farm marketings. This means that about 90 per cent of these benefits go to the top 1.5 million farms. It is reasonable to assume that the capitalization of a portion of these subsidies into farmland values also occurs in about the same pattern. Therefore, the poor people in farming, living on the poorer farms, probably are not gaining enough wealth in the form of the their farm property to change the general picture of their poverty.

Solutions to the farm poverty problem obviously must be sought in other directions from that of the commercial farm programs. The problem is at root one of *underemployment*. People living on the low-

The government operates training services for all members of the farm family. Young 4-H Club members learn the best methods of modern farming by raising livestock and completing other practical projects. Left, a girl

income farms are fully occupied, but they are unproductively occupied. The Economic Research Service of the Department of Agriculture estimates that in 1959 underemployment in agriculture amounted to the equivalent of 1.3 million wholly unemployed workers. The 5 million persons counted as unemployed by the Department of Labor in 1964 do not represent the full extent of unemployment so long as many people on farms are earning so little.

Agriculture is a free enterprise industry which is easy to enter, on a subsistence level. It therefore acts as a backstop for industrial unemployment.

There is no real solution for the poverty sector of agriculture

from Madison County, Montana, displays her prizewinning Hereford calves. Right, a Henry County, Missouri, 4-H leader demonstrates how to remove the needle teeth on pigs.

within agriculture itself. The only solution is a higher rate of national economic growth to provide more jobs for young people in rural areas. The ideal solution is the development of new factories and other businesses in rural areas to absorb the excess farm-labor supply. But this is not always feasible.

Programs to improve educational opportunities in rural areas are badly needed. The vocational education available in most farming areas is primarily that justly famed agricultural education, yet the majority of young people cannot find openings in agriculture and must seek work elsewhere.

Public efforts to improve the opportunities for people in low-in-

[161]

come farming areas have been halfhearted and inadequately financed. The poverty problem in agriculture is like poverty elsewhere. It is a welfare problem and demands a welfare approach.

The federal Rural Area Development program has been gathering momentum in recent years and is expected to get more attention in the future under President Johnson's antipoverty program. Migration from agriculture has been heavily from the southern states and other low-income farming areas. As people leave these areas to take jobs in nonfarm occupations, capable farmers are able to enlarge their farms, obtain credit for capital expansion, and move into the realm of commercial farming.

The attack on rural poverty is a desirable development, but no one should be misled that it is a solution to the commercial agriculture problem. The lower half of agriculture produces less than 10 per cent of the supply of farm products for market. Commercial agriculture will continue to be troubled with surpluses and a cost-price squeeze regardless of what adjustments are made in noncommercial farming.

Solving the low-income problem in agriculture and obtaining a healthier adjustment of manpower to resources cannot be achieved without an active nonfarm employment market. Higher farm-price supports and production controls are largely irrelevant for the problems of low-income, subsistence agriculture.

So don't argue that farm subsidies are misdirected and fail to solve the farm-poverty problem. You miss the point. The farm-income supports never were intended to change the distribution of income and wealth within agriculture. They were intended to raise the entire level of income from farm production, and they have done so. The whole package of public spending on agriculture has stimulated technical advance and improved labor efficiency, thus making many farm workers redundant. Finding new jobs for these workers, training them for new occupations, and easing their transition out of farming is a separate task which must be undertaken by other means than farm-income supports.

16 / FARM ADJUSTMENT
AND THE NATION

AGRICULTURE IS in a period of rapid adjustment. In nonfarm industry we now call the process "automation." In farming, for some reason, we call it "adjustment."

The word has come to have a current flavor, a fashionable flavor. Everybody talks about agricultural adjustment as if it were something new or peculiar to our times. But of course agriculture has been adjusting since the beginning of civilization. The whole process of economic advancement begins with reducing the amount of human effort it takes to provide the basic necessities of life—and then using the workpower thus released to produce other kinds of goods, more comfortable living, more leisure, the arts.

The upsurge in farm productivity in the last century has been phenomenal (see chapters 8 and 9). The effect of this revolution on the economic growth of this country and on the rest of the world has not been well enough appreciated. Credit for economic progress usually has gone to manufacturing, transportation, and other so-called secondary and tertiary occupations.

But if agriculture had not become more productive, so that fewer people were needed to produce food, industrial development would not have been possible. We always speak about economic development as the process of expanding industrial output, services, and nonfarm business. Yet we might with equal accuracy talk about it as the process of transferring people out of farming.

The impact of agricultural adjustment on the nation, then, is to make available the extra human resources for a richer standard of living.

If this were better understood—the important, in fact *essential*, part that agriculture has played and still plays in making the country richer—then we would do better about seeing to it that farm people share equally in that higher level of living, because we do believe in this country in equal rewards for equal work.

When a country has 80 per cent or even 50 per cent of its labor engaged in farming, one can make a strong argument that the country should place major emphasis on improving agriculture. Also one can say that in such a situation there should be a strong effort to attract people out of farming into other occupations. But today in the United States these are matters of relatively small importance.

In other words the impact of agricultural adjustment on the nation now is slight, compared with what it has been in the past. And that is one of our main farm problems today. Farmers have worked themselves out of a job, in a manner of speaking, and out of the center of public concern.

The total labor force in this country in 1964 was around 77 million, including members of the armed forces. Less than 6 million of these 77 million were in farming, or about 7 per cent. Rather large changes in this agricultural work force would have comparatively little significance in the total picture.

Only 1 in 5 additions to the United States urban population came from farms between 1940 and 1950. The proportion declined from this level in the 1950-60 decade to about 1 in 6 and will be even less in the future. Industry, trades, and services no longer depend largely upon emigrants from agriculture for most of their work force.

To get a clearer sense of the effect of agricultural adjustment on the nation, let us say that the number of people in farm work were reduced by 2 million from 1964 to 1969. This would be a reduction in the farm labor supply at more than twice the rate of the 1950-60 decade. It would be a decrease of about 35 per cent in 5 years, as compared with 25 per cent in the last 10 years.

Overproduction of wheat is dramatically illustrated by these storage bins near Lincoln, Nebraska. The cylindrical tanks hold five million bushels; the steel buildings at the left hold an additional two and one half million bushels.

Even this massive change in farming, which most of us would agree is unlikely to occur, would be only a 2½ *per cent* addition to the nonfarm labor force.

The contrast to observe here is between the farm adjustment needs of a poor economy and those of an advanced industrial economy.

The inefficiency of having two or three million underemployed people in farming is a matter of small consequence in the United States economy. It makes little difference in the total output of our economic system whether the surplus workers in agriculture stay there or move out.

In much of Asia, Africa, and Latin America, the problem of agricultural adjustment is vital. These areas are economically in about the same position that we were at the time of the Revolution. But in the United States today we cannot say that farm adjustment is vital.

The movement of workers out of farming may make a lot of difference in the nonfarm labor market when unemployment is high, as it was in 1963. Two million people from agriculture added to the total nonfarm work force would not have a huge impact. But let us compare these 2 million displaced farm workers with the number of *unemployed,* which was about 4 to 5 million in the early 1960s. Obviously, adding 2 million to the number of people seeking work in nonfarm jobs would be quite a jolt.

In the practical situation of the United States today, we must recognize that, so long as there are sizable numbers of unemployed in the cities, agriculture performs a public welfare function by keeping excess people on farms beyond the requirements of the industry. From the public viewpoint agriculture keeps down the rolls of unemployed in the cities—and also the public expenditures for relief in the cities.

Thus one might argue that it is more economic to maintain surplus labor in agriculture than to speed up agricultural adjustment. In short the public may be said to have a stake in *stopping* agricultural adjustment at the moment.

And even in the longer run, since there are no great economic gains to be made for the country as a whole by further migration from farms to cities, why not just let agriculture alone? Why not maintain a surplus of labor in farming, since this makes a good shock-absorber for the rest of the economy?

This is an appealing idea to many small-town businessmen and to those with vested interests in rural institutions, including small-town schools. They don't like to see their farmers dwindling in numbers. We have a whole governmental system in many states based on a rural society, and there are many resistances to changing it. Heavy costs are involved in the reorganization of schools, local governments, and local businesses, caused by the decline in farm population.

Maybe it would be cheaper for the country to subsidize the present farm population, even to the extent that average incomes were

Because of a lack of permanent space, many farmers are forced to pile part of their crops on the ground, making it ineligible for government loans. Here a Montgomery County, Iowa, farmer stands on a pile of corn—the overflow of his adequately stored surplus on which he received a Commodity Credit Corporation loan.

U.S. Department of Agriculture

hoisted as high as for the nonfarm population, rather than continue with agricultural adjustment. This is not an entirely facetious suggestion.

It is conceivable that the American public might prefer to maintain an agriculture of about the present size, with a family-type farm organization, for social and cultural reasons. Perhaps it would be worth the cost of the subsidies to preserve a rural culture, if such a thing still exists, especially if you stop to consider the costs of reorganizing the whole rural society to a much smaller-sized farming industry.

Now let's come down out of the clouds. This idea of stopping agricultural adjustment is ridiculous. You can't stop progress. Farmers themselves don't want to preserve a rural culture—they are trying as hard as they can to live like people in the cities. And the only way this goal will be achieved is to reduce the number of people in farming. The people of this country are not going to spend a great deal more money for food, either in the market or in government subsidies. Everybody is too well fed to spend more. So the primary way farm people can increase their average income is to reduce the number of farm-income receivers.

The general public is not vitally concerned with this problem from an economic viewpoint. But it does have a deep, long-run concern in farm adjustment from the viewpoint of equal opportunity. The young people growing up on the poorest farms will not be assets to the country in the future. They will lack education, job training, social adjustment, and even the health of their contemporaries in the cities. Advocates of country life often say that it is a healthier life than in the cities, but this is no longer true for the country as a whole. Military draft records show that health is poorer on the average in farming areas than in cities. Farm boys may get more fresh air, but they have poorer medical and hospital facilities, and even their diets apparently aren't as good. This is for the nation as a whole, of course, and includes the mass rural poverty of the south.

So it is in the public interest to stimulate agricultural adjustment, to provide better opportunity for rural young people. It is in the public interest from the viewpoint of social justice and equality. The economic benefit to the society from better agricultural adjustment may be small —but the *moral* benefit from living up to our ideals is large.

17 / THE POLITICS
OF AGRICULTURE

FARMERS AND THEIR LEADERS are voicing deep concern these days about the decline of agriculture's political power. Nearly every farm organization leader complains in his speeches that the farmer is losing his influence in the national government and in the state governments, because of the decline in the number and proportion of farm voters.

Some agricultural leaders have been saying that the present session of Congress or the next may be the "last chance" of farmers to get an effective government program which will give agriculture fair bargaining power in the economy. They say city congressmen will no longer vote for legislation to help farmers.

When these farm spokesmen express alarm about the loss of political power for agriculture they are making two assumptions: (1) that farmers are united behind some one program or are in search of a common objective, and (2) that there is strong city resistance to the program farmers are seeking.

Before we examine these assumptions, let us outline the changes now occurring in the American political scene so far as representation of farm people in government is concerned.

It is certainly true that the so-called "farmer vote" is shrinking and has been shrinking for a long time. The nation has been growing more urban and less rural, and the rate of change has been speeding up during the last quarter-century. This inevitably means that government in a democracy increasingly reflects the urban viewpoint—and in cases where city and farm views clash, the city view carries more weight.

The rapid adoption of new technology in American agriculture, has reduced the farm work force and the farm population. People have been leaving agriculture in great numbers, especially since 1940. Many of the small towns and rural areas also have lost population, and towns even have disappeared in some cases. Many congressional districts that have been predominantly rural now are predominantly made up of people living in cities.

The proportion of rural and farm population to the total has been falling off at an amazing rate. America now is a highly urbanized country, almost as urbanized as such workshop countries as England and Belgium. The trend has not ended. In this decade of the 1960s the United States is likely to have a population increase of at least 30 million. Metropolitan areas will get around 25 million of this increase. The other 5 million, plus a continued flow of people from rural areas, will be added to urban areas of lesser size.

This radical transformation of the United States from a mainly rural society to an urban one in the last half-century has disrupted many old institutions, habits, and customs—not least among these being the institutions of government and the political system.

Actually the changes in politics and government have not yet caught up with the massive switchover of the population. The seats in the federal Congress and the state legislatures still greatly overrepresent rural areas and farm people. Economic change has been far outstripping governmental change.

It is true that some reforms have occurred in the makeup of legislatures, but the big alteration in rural representation is yet to come. It has been possible in many states for as few as 20 or 30 per cent of the people to control majorities in their legislatures. Representative districts have not been adjusted to take account of the movement of people from small towns and farms to the cities. In Iowa, for example, as late as 1962 our legislators were elected from districts based on the distribution of population of about 1900.

U.S. Department of Agriculture

Each year the United States exports 500 million bushels of wheat to under-developed countries under the Food for Peace program. An important part of our foreign policy, Food for Peace benefits American farmers by removing some of their surplus. Above, wheat being unloaded in Pakistan.

The movement for legislative reapportionment is illustrated by the developments in Iowa. A constitutional amendment to change the legislative districts passed the legislature in 1961 and 1963, but was rejected as inadequate by the people in a referendum. A special session of the legislature in 1964, in response to the referendum and a federal court decision, passed a new temporary reapportionment plan which was much more representative in both houses. It was signed by the governor, but it was ruled unconstitutional by the federal court. The

1965 legislature thereupon passed another "temporary" plan providing almost equal population districts. And it inaugurated a new "permanent" plan carrying out this principle. This must be passed by another session and a vote of the people before it becomes effective.

In March 1962, the United States Supreme Court ruled that voters can seek relief in the federal courts from unfair representation in their state legislatures. This means that underrepresented city groups can file lawsuits in the federal courts seeking court orders to require more representation in their state legislatures. The basic principle behind the Supreme Court decision is that every citizen has a right under the United States Constitution to an equal voice in his government, including state government. If some voters have proportionally fewer representatives than others, then they are being denied their rights to an equal voice. In a 1964 decision the Court reaffirmed this view in more conclusive language and said, in effect, that significant departure from representation proportional to population in either house of a state legislature was unconstitutional. The states had already begun to act in response to the 1962 decision. Dozens of lawsuits had been filed in 39 of the 50 states by November 1963. The courts had already invalidated legislative districting in at least 20 states by the end of 1963. As a result of the 1964 Court decision this process will be speeded up.

It had been only a question of time before legislative representation would have to take into account the changing character of the American population. In a democratic society such grossly unfair representation could not last. The Supreme Court decision brought to a head somewhat earlier what was coming to a head anyway.

The reapportionment of seats in state legislatures will affect the House of Representatives in Congress, because the state legislatures determine congressional election districts. In February 1964 the Supreme Court also ruled that representatives in Congress should represent approximately equal numbers of people.

Each state gets its proportion of members in the House of Representatives on the basis of its population. That is a requirement of the United States Constitution. And a reapportionment of these representatives among the states is made after each 10-year census. But within a state, a legislature has been able to juggle the district lines as it saw fit. Usually this was done to favor the political party in control of the legislature; for example, it was done a few years ago in California to favor the Democrats and in New York to favor the Republicans. Historically farm representation has been favored in almost every state, because the legislatures themselves have been weighted with rural members.

Now, as we have noted, many farm spokesmen view the forthcoming change in legislative representation as a disaster. They fear that governmental decisions will go against the farm population. However, the unfair overrepresentation of rural areas has led to tensions and conflicts between city people and rural people. City people have resented the fact that farm organizations have fought to maintain their power in the assemblies. If city people begin to feel they are getting a square deal in their representation in government, much of their antagonism to farm groups may disappear.

It has not been the farm organizations alone that have opposed reform of state legislatures. Conservative business groups have teamed up with the farm groups to maintain the status quo. Often farmers have been only the pawns in a fight by conservative business groups against reform. They have played up farm-city antagonism in order to oppose public housing, urban redevelopment, and welfare legislation.

Rural legislatures often have blocked legislation which the expanding cities wanted. They have tried to keep the old and familiar institutions and to halt the urbanization trend. But in doing so they often have hurt the real interests of the farming population. As the farm population declines the need for local government institutions changes. With good roads and rapid transportation fewer and larger schools are practical. Education in rural areas has strongly emphasized

U.S. Department of Agriculture

One advantage of our nation's surplus is that it is readily available for relief, either in America or overseas. Left, flour and other food packages

agricultural training for young people. Yet most young farm people are moving to the cities because of lack of openings in agriculture. They need education for industrial occupations.

Legislatures that are more representative of the people in cities will make changes in such policies. These changes will not be to the disadvantage of rural people. They will encourage faster economic development, which will mean a healthier agriculture as well as healthier cities. Interests of city and country are growing closer all the time in a modern society.

[174]

U.S. Department of Agriculture

are distributed to poverty-stricken areas. Right, prepared food is served to flood victims.

On the national scene it is apparent that the old farm "bloc" has broken up and that the influence of city representatives in agricultural policy is growing stronger. If farmers were united behind a particular set of agricultural policies, and if they were being denied action by a Congress dominated by city interests, that would be something to worry about. However, there is little evidence either that farmers agree on what they want or that urban representatives are opposed to farm interests.

The farm organizations are so far apart on agricultural policy

[175]

that it is impossible for city congressmen to tell what agriculture wants. Even if we should assume that Congress was willing to give agriculture anything it wanted, who could speak for the industry?

The American Farm Bureau Federation is the largest of the general farm organizations, with about one and a half million members. The Farm Bureau has become a very conservative organization. In general it opposes government programs to control production and marketing of farm products and to support prices, although in 1933-38 it was the leading pressure group for such programs. The Farm Bureau usually agrees with such business organizations as the National Association of Manufacturers and the United States Chamber of Commerce. It has strongly opposed the farm policies of the Kennedy and Johnson administrations and was sympathetic to the policies of the Eisenhower administration.

The Farm Bureau got its start as a semiofficial organization associated with the state agricultural colleges to carry out extension educational programs. It did not begin as a "protest" group as the other farm organizations did. It owes its existence to federal and state government activity in agriculture, but it has now become strongly anti-government in its viewpoint.

The National Farmers Union advocates a high degree of government management of agricultural production, prices, and distribution. The Farmers Union, with about 400,000 members, represents the "left wing" in agricultural affairs and usually backs the policies of the Democratic party. It supported the Kennedy administration program for agriculture and would prefer an even more vigorous effort to control farm production and raise prices of farm products.

The National Grange, the third major farm organization, has about 500,000 members. Like the Farmers Union, it got its start as an organization of farm discontent. It is the oldest of the organizations, dating back to the farm depression following the Civil War. It fought the railroads and the new industrial trusts in an effort to get a fair deal for farmers.

In the present political scene the Grange stands somewhere between the Farm Bureau and the Farmers Union in its general approach to farm policies. However, it usually supported the programs of the Kennedy administration. It is much more agreeable to government action in behalf of agriculture than is the Farm Bureau.

In the last few years the new National Farmers Organization (NFO) has grown up, largely in the middle west. The NFO wants to achieve market bargaining power for farmers by their own efforts. It tries to organize farmers to conduct "strikes," to withhold their commodities from market. Several attempts of this kind have been unsuccessful. However, NFO continues to appeal to many farmers, and appears to be holding or increasing its membership.

Thus, as we look over the general farm organizations, we find a chaotic picture of agricultural politics.

Let us compare this situation with that affecting organized labor. Labor unions have their disputes, sometimes very bitter ones. But when it comes to major issues of national policy the labor unions are able to form a solid front. They were all opposed to the Taft-Hartley law which established certain limitations on labor-union bargaining power. They also oppose the so-called "right to work" laws. These are laws which have been adopted in many states to outlaw labor-union contracts which require all employees of a factory to belong to the union. The labor unions are united on most federal welfare programs, federal aid to education, and similar programs.

Business groups also quarrel among themselves about many policies. But on the major questions, the National Association of Manufacturers, the Chamber of Commerce, and other leading business organizations generally stand together.

Congress knows what the business viewpoint is, and it knows what the labor viewpoint is. But no one knows where the agriculture industry stands.

Obviously there are bound to be sharp differences of viewpoint between cotton growers and livestock producers. Organizations representing these different commodity interests within agriculture have different viewpoints about farm policies, just as there are different industrial viewpoints among business and labor groups. But on the major questions which affect the industry as a whole, there is no common ground among farm organizations.

This complicates farm policy-making, and it is surprising that the total results for farmers and the public have been as good as they have been. Perhaps the squabbles help, after all, and prevent wild departures of government into extreme remedies for the "farm problem."

18 / FARM POLICY CHOICES

Whatever else America's national farm policy may have done, it has provided both abundance and rapid technical progress, which are of great value to the nation. The nation should not expect agriculture, with 10 per cent of the population, to bear a major share of the cost of these contributions to the nation. To turn agriculture over to the free market would be like expecting General Dynamics, General Motors, and General Electric to produce jet aircraft and missiles at less than cost—and their workers to accept a 50 per cent cut in wages for work on national defense.

By accident, by luck, by compensating errors, and by pragmatic trial and error, instead of extreme doctrinaire solutions, United States national agricultural policy has accomplished reasonably good results all around. The horror stories and predictions of disaster have not been borne out in practice.

Theoretical *laissez-faire* economists said, for example, in 1933 that the production controls Henry A. Wallace was "imposing" on farmers would bring dire results: Improvements in production technology would be stifled; agriculture would be frozen into a pattern by the use of historical acreage bases for crop allotments; changes in size of farm, regional shifts in crops and livestock would be halted at the expense of efficiency. These calamities have not occurred. The rate of technical advance has speeded up during the era of the crop-control and price-support programs.

In the 20 years from 1920 to 1940, farm output increased at the rate of 1.1 per cent a year. In the 15 years from 1940 to 1955 it rose at the rate of 2 per cent a year. This rate of increase has continued since 1955 in spite of the diversion of large acreages of grains and other crops to conservation uses or complete idling. The Economic Research Service of the Department of Agriculture estimates that in the absence of these acreage-diversion programs, production would have increased at the rate of 3.5 per cent a year.

The increase in production for human use from 1920 to 1940 came about largely from a reduction in horses and mules (land used for feeding them could be used for human food) plus an increase in crop production per acre and a rise in livestock production. There was little change in total crop acreage. From 1940 to 1955 the advance in production was caused by a faster rise in crop production per acre, plus a further advance in livestock production and a continuing decline in horse and mule power. Since then there have been practically no gains from replacement of horses and mules, but crop output per acre has climbed even more sharply, more than offsetting a large cut in crop acreage, and livestock production has continued to advance.

As for the expectation that acreage controls would prevent interregional shifts of crops in pursuit of least-cost production, look at corn.

Between 1937 and 1960 total corn acreage dropped from 94 million to 82 million. Corn acreage declined by 12 million in the south-central states and 4 million in the south Atlantic states, areas of low yield. In the corn belt, the area of most efficient production, there was an increase of 3 million acres.

Cotton production has moved westward to more efficient producing areas despite the acreage-control program.

James O. Bray and Patricia Watkins, of Stanford University, show convincingly in a study * on technical change in corn production that price supports, rather than being detrimental to economic growth,

* "Technical Change in Corn Production in the United States, 1870-1960," *Journal of Farm Economics* (November 1964).

caused new techniques to be adopted more rapidly and high-cost producers to be retired sooner than otherwise would have been the case.
The most rapid rate of technical change ever experiencd in the
United States in corn production occurred during a period when price
supports for corn were in full effect.

Bray and Watkins make a distinction between growth in agricultural production caused by improvement of extractive techniques or
fertility-depleting operations and that caused by soil-restorative techniques. Among the extractive techniques are replacement of animal and
human power by mechanical power and biological improvements such
as hybrid corn. The limit of improvement from extractive techniques
is the natural fertility barrier. Such traditional restorative techniques
as crop rotation may lift the fertility barrier slightly. But the real
breakthrough in corn production came during the early 1940s from
the introduction of artificially manufactured, cheap nitrogen. The
yield potential in hybrid corn could not have been realized without
this innovation in fertilization that has lifted the fertility barrier. We
do not know yet how high this barrier can be raised.

America's national farm policy of shielding agriculture from the
dynamic forces of supply and demand was not adopted with the idea
that it would facilitate economic development. But the programs
proved to be an important force for modernization of agriculture.
They provided the assurance of future prices farmers needed to make
the investment in fertilizer.

The weakness of our farm policy as we look ahead is that the
rewards for hard work, managerial competence, initiative, and enterprise in farming are not high enough, in comparison with the rest of
the economy. This is true by the standard of equality of opportunity
and the standard of welfare equity. It is also true from the viewpoint
of the national interest in maintaining a high quality of brains in the
agricultural industry. As farming becomes increasingly complex, more
scientific and less traditional, we shall have to attract and keep able
people in the business. The country will have to pay for this. Economic

incentive in agriculture must be raised if the magnificent progress of this industry is to be maintained. The free market, unassisted by government, is incapable of providing this incentive.

A policy of moderately higher incomes in commercial agriculture will not stop the migration of high-cost producers out of the industry. Migration from agriculture in recent years has been almost entirely from the lower end of the scale in size of farm, level of income, level of education, and level of production. This migration should continue.

If the nation should decide to redirect farm policy with the objective of raising farm income, what are the choices?

The intellectual foundation for making such decisions has been enormously enhanced in the last dozen years or so. The land-grant agricultural colleges, the U.S. Department of Agriculture, and some of the private universities have been increasing our stockpile of imaginative research and original thinking on agricultural policy.* It is no longer accurate to accuse the agricultural colleges of ignoring the economic adjustment problems of agriculture in their studies. These institutions have gone far toward lifting us out of the realm of faith and traditionalism in our policy thinking.

We may obtain from recent studies dependable projections of the consequences to farm income and to the federal budget of various changes in farm policy. If we set a certain target of farm income, these scholars can tell us with considerable precision how much the cost will be for various types of programs, in terms of consumer expenditures in the market and federal taxes.

Fortunately the United States is rich enough that it can choose over a wide range of farm policy. Americans can afford to pay for a high degree of voluntariness and few regulations, if that is what the people want, and still maintain high farm income.

There can be no question but that the way to achieve a given

---

* Iowa State University at Ames and North Carolina State University at Raleigh have established special centers for agricultural policy research and education under grants from the Kellogg Foundation. These institutions have taken a position of leadership in the land-grant university system in this field.

level of farm income at the least governmental cost is through production control. The most expensive way to reach a given income target in terms of government cost is through direct subsidies.*

The farm-income support programs have been compromises between these extremes. Farm income has been raised partly by production restraints and supply management, which increased the prices to consumers in the market, and partly by direct subsidies from government.

These compromises do not please the absolutists who want to go all the way to government supply management or the reverse. But they are quite practical in a democratic political system. In operation of the farm programs it has been found that limited production controls and voluntary programs, even if that means a lower level of price support, are preferable to high price supports and strict controls.

If we seek a higher farm-income goal, we can (1) increase the government's budget for direct subsidies to farmers or (2) tighten production controls to increase returns in the market or (3) elevate price supports without tightening production controls and run heavier government costs in management and disposal of surpluses.

The extent to which one or a combination of these methods must be used to reach a given income target depends partly on (1) how much expansion in foreign commercial sales of farm products can be achieved and (2) how large a quantity of these products is used in foreign aid (Food for Peace) programs.

The need for government programs also depends on whether or not effective supply management can be accomplished by private farm organizations. If farmer bargaining power can be strengthened through private organizational arrangements, less government control will be needed. Marketing orders and agreements supervised by the federal

---

* See *A National Farm Program for Feed Grains and Wheat,* National Planning Association, June 1964. Also, *Farm Program Alternatives: Farm Incomes and Public Costs Under Alternative Programs for Feed Grains and Wheat,* May, 1963, by Luther G. Tweeten, Earl O. Heady, and Leo V. Mayer, Center for Agricultural and Economic Development, Iowa State University.

government work well in balancing market supplies of some commodities—as long as total grain output is held in check by government programs.

An argument for tightening government production controls is often made on the practical ground that the public is likely to object less to a rise of food costs in the market than to a highly visible increase in the government budget. Returning to a higher level of price supports without controls would bring back the complications in surplus management that were regarded as scandalous a few years ago. High price supports with unrestrained production tend to bring on "dumping" practices in foreign trade which run counter to United States trade policy.

Is a policy of increasing the effectiveness of production controls and raising market prices to consumers politically feasible? If the question refers to acceptance by the general public, it seems to me the answer clearly is Yes. There has been a great deal of talk in farming circles in recent years about "poor public relations," "bad press for agriculture," and the like. But a search through published materials, of the past decade, of labor unions, consumer groups, and urban groups failed to produce significant examples of protest against farmers because of high food costs.*

As a matter of fact the AFL-CIO usually has backed farm-income support legislation in Congress. Consumer and urban groups, to the extent that they have taken an interest in agriculture at all, have been more concerned with the problems of poverty in agriculture, migratory farm labor, and the absence of welfare legislation for farm workers than in food prices. The National Consumers League, for example, testifying in Congress on farm labor and rural poverty in 1964, argued that the consumer could well afford the slight increase in cost of food that might accrue through providing a minimum wage and better living conditions for farm laborers.

* Prof. Don Hadwiger of the Political Science Department of Iowa State University helped to make this review of the literature. I am grateful to him for this assistance, but he bears no responsibility for the conclusions reached here.

The National School Lunch Program, sponsored by the Department of Agriculture and state and local governments, serves 13.5 million boys and girls in schools across the country. Children who buy the lunches eat nutritious food at reduced prices. In Rye, New York, where this picture was taken, they pay only three cents for a one-third quart container of milk.

The truth is that practically all the objection to farm production controls comes from farm organizations, principally the Farm Bureau, and agriculture-related industries (which have a stake in large-volume farm production) and from theorists who see such regulations as beyond the pale of prescribed doctrine of free enterprise. Farm organizations in some cases have argued that consumer antagonism required a reduction in farm controls. There has been talk of farm price-support legislation being a "bread tax" on consumers. So far as I have been able to find, this protest does not come from consumers.

[185]

Urban congressmen, however, may well object to large government expenditures for agriculture in the budget. They may insist on a stiffer blend of production control in the farm program "mix." Their complaints on farm legislation are not about farm income being raised beyond a reasonable level but about the *method used* to raise farm income. They may argue more and more in the future that if farmers are to be guaranteed a certain level of prices, there must be a limit to how much they can produce at that price.

Very likely we will continue to employ a blend of methods of supporting farm income, either adding more control and cutting subsidies or adding more subsidy while reducing restrictions if the federal budgetary hurdle can be surmounted.

In making decisions on future directions of farm policy, it is to be hoped that we can avoid excessive attention to doctrine and moral philosophy, which leads to absolutist policies. We Americans, in our practical wisdom, frequently make fun of the Russians for their obsession with doctrinal considerations—and rightly so. The lopsided development of the Soviet economy, especially the dismal results in agriculture, plainly are a consequence, in part, of adherence to the various Marxist dogmas about economic organization, ownership of resources, and pricing. We should be wary that we don't get trapped in the same way by doctrine.

Farm policies are not morally right or wrong. They are right if they accomplish the agreed national objectives and wrong if they don't.

19 / AMERICAN AGRICULTURE AND THE DEVELOPING COUNTRIES

CAN THE TRIUMPH of American agricultural productivity be repeated in other countries? Can the American experience be adapted to other lands?

The answer is that it *is* being adapted and extended around the world.

European countries are well along in their own "industrial revolution in agriculture." When America was a young country it borrowed scientific knowledge about farming from Europe. American farmers were helped by the experience of the older countries. Most of the livestock of the United States originally came from Europe, including the British Isles, along with the best practices of husbandry developed there. In recent years the exchange of information has been going the other way. American agriculture has been repaying its debt of knowledge to European agriculture. European farmers have been making great strides in productivity by adapting American experience to their own conditions and needs.

The same may be said for Japan. Japanese farmers, with their renowned diligence and ability to learn, have been adopting new methods with sensational results. The land-reform program after World War II, which broke up the large estates and gave individual farmers the opportunity to cultivate their own land, has been a great success. Japanese agriculture has become a model for Asia.

Other countries, less industrially developed than Japan, are beginning agricultural-improvement programs, partly modeled on the successful experience of America. In many of them, farm research and educational systems, similar to those of the United States, are being organized. There is no reason why they cannot match America in farming, given time, the will, and help from the United States.

This help Americans are glad to extend. Farmers in all lands are neighborly people and have a long tradition of help to one another which reaches across national boundaries. There is a feeling of comradeship and understanding among farmers that breaks through language and other barriers. In the post-World War II years America has established a mighty effort, both public and private, to assist less privileged countries to develop productive farming industries. Through the United Nations Food and Agricultural Organization, through the United States foreign-aid program, through private educational agencies, through churches, and through individual business programs, farmers in other countries are being taught how American farmers have become so productive.

Every country has different customs, traditions, and governmental machinery—and different natural resources. Native crops, livestock, and food likes and dislikes vary. So the American experience obviously cannot be exactly duplicated anywhere. The emphasis must be on adaptation, not imitation.

For example, the family-farm system which has worked so well in the United States is not necessarily the only organization which can develop a productive agriculture. Cooperative farms may work well in some countries. Various styles of contract farming may work in others.

One overriding factor does seem essential. Whatever the kind of farm organization, there must be *incentives* for the farmer to farm efficiently. There must be freedom for experimentation and application of different farming ideas farm by farm. Attempts to regiment farmers into large organizations and to direct farming from a national center have been uniformly unsuccessful.

No country can leap from hand-work farming to machine farming in a year or two. It took the United States many decades of intensified

The United States is a country of independent family farms. In other parts of the world many farmers live in villages and work on collective or corporate farms. But in America most farmers live and work on their own land. Above, a dairy farm in Tillamook County, Oregon.

educational effort before a real momentum of agricultural progress was developed. After the organization of public institutions devoted to farm research and education, scientific knowledge began to accumulate. But farmers were slow to adopt the new methods at first. It has been only in the last 50 years that American agriculture has made big strides. And it has been largely in the last 20 years that the greatest strides have been taken.

So countries with traditional farming populations and farming methods should not expect to accomplish an agricultural revolution right away. But with large investments, both public and private, much can be accomplished amazingly fast.

Other countries do not have to take all the steps the United States has taken in achieving the levels of output per man which exist in America today. They can skip over some farming methods which have been discarded in the United States. For example, they can move from hand harvesting of grain to the combine, without stopping at the intermediate stage of the stationary thresher. They can learn from American mistakes as well as successes.

But learning about new farm methods is the smallest part of the job. The important thing to learn is how to *develop* new farm methods applied to the needs and purposes of the individual country. That means research stations and educational institutions.

Even more important are the *idea of progress* itself and the *concrete incentives* to make progress.

America's biggest advantage in agricultural development, perhaps, was a set of ideas. These ideas might be called a belief in the inevitability of progress. The ideas came from an exceptional group of early leaders of the new American republic and from a heritage of freedom and independence.

Americans have always believed that they could do anything if they worked hard enough, studied hard enough, and sacrificed enough. This set of beliefs cannot be exported—it must be *imported*. It cannot be imposed or indoctrinated—it must be *adopted*.

Since the close of a catastrophic second world war of this century, a new urgency has arisen for speeding world economic development and widening the benefits from it. Men everywhere have come to realize that a world one-third rich and two-thirds poor cannot stand. Revolutionary movements seek to narrow the wealth gap by violence and conquest, and the contest between persuasion and force as methods of generating economic progress has not yet been decided.

It is a matter of national pride that the United States has been first among the advanced nations to see this crisis and to act on it. Out of concern for the welfare of mankind, long characteristic of the American people—as well as immediate self-interest—the United States has provided grants, loans, and technical assistance on a large scale to other countries.

Foreign aid, we call it, but it is not a mere sharing of wealth; nor is it exploitive economic colonialism. It is unique in the relations of strong nations to weak. It is a concerted attempt to build self-sustaining economic systems, capable of growth under their own power and capable of sustaining free governments. It may be the work for which the United States will be best known and remembered by generations to come.

At first, in the period after World War II, the emphasis was on rehabilitation and recovery of devastated countries, largely those in industrialized Europe. In the last decade the effort has been redirected toward developing the underdeveloped countries of Asia, Africa, and Latin America. Our experience in this endeavor is limited. Dramatic successes, like the revival of Europe, are not forthcoming and not to be expected. The problems are complex and not well understood. We are creating a whole new science of economic development as we go along.

But we have now reached a point in experience with foreign aid when it is possible to apply lessons learned, to remodel and readjust, to make sure that we are using our resources as wisely as possible in this great national task.

Human well-being is not wholly a matter of material plenty. But higher material production per person is an essential foundation for pursuing the better life of individual freedom, absence of fear, and the opportunity for men to control their destiny.

In their haste and anxiety to "join the modern world," leaders of many of the less developed countries have become fascinated with mass-production factories, electric power, big buildings, sports arenas, hotels, and other appurtenances of the advanced economic systems. It is not surprising. These are not mere symbols; they are important elements of a high-production economy. But the danger is that this concentration on industrialization and showy construction neglects the one vital necessity for economic progress in a poor country: an improving agriculture. Some of the biggest mistakes in economic development—on the part of countries furnishing aid, including the United States, as well as by the developing countries themselves—have been made in the diversion of capital investment and technical expertise away from agriculture.

In countries with inadequate food supplies for good diets, clearly agriculture must have priority in development, just to provide the energy and resistance to disease that make it possible for people to work effectively.

In countries with 70 or 80 per cent of the people engaged in farming, the only practical way to increase output per worker is to increase agricultural productivity.

In countries with inadequate capital resources and with most of the people employed in agriculture, clearly capital accumulation can be achieved only through higher production in agriculture.

In countries dependent on imports for a richer consumption standard and with most of the people in farming, clearly expanded agricultural output for export is the key to higher consumption.

It is true that some of the countries in these categories can profitably concentrate on production of minerals, nonfood crops, and other exportable goods, thus earning the foreign exchange to import part of their food supply. Not every country should try to produce all the food it needs for its own consumption.

But our experience so far indicates that the errors in development planning, in allocation of resources, and in research-educational effort are more likely to be in the slighting of food production than in overdoing it.

Food production per person in some of the poorest countries of the world has not been making enough progress to keep ahead of population increases. The United Nations Food and Agriculture Organization has estimated that one-sixth of the world's population (500 million people) suffers from active hunger and another one-third suffers diet deficiencies and malnutrition. Population in most of these countries is growing at the rate of 2.5 to 3 per cent a year. FAO estimates that to achieve in the 1963-73 decade the modest food-consumption goal of about 2,400 calories per person per day will require an increase of 45 per cent in food production in Africa and 52 per cent in the Far East.

Countries in Asia, Africa, and Latin America making up two-thirds of the world's population in 1959 produced only $180 billion worth of goods and services, according to the United Nations. This was little more than a third of the gross national product of the United States in that year. Per-capita production ranged from $50 per year in some places in Africa to nearly $300 in some countries such as Mexico which are on the way to self-sustaining growth.

If the poorer countries are not to sink further into poverty and despair, they must find ways to increase agricultural output dramatically. That is not easy—even with the best of intentions and the best of will on the part of the high-producing countries to help them.

The United States unquestionably is the best fitted of all countries to guide and assist the improvement of agricultural productivity in the world. The rise in America's agricultural productivity, especially under the impetus of the scientific-technological revolution of the last quarter-century, has been one of the major factors in our general economic advance. It is in the area of farm production that our results contrast most sharply with those of the Communist countries. While the Soviet Union and China are plagued with food shortages and waste of resources in farming, the United States enjoys the best average diets in the world and still can provide quantities of grain and other farm products as foreign aid to needy countries. In the technology of many types of agriculture, ranging across a whole continent, from subtropical to near desert to near frigid, United States supremacy is undisputed.

The United States has not been applying its knowledge and experience in agricultural development as fully as it should in its aid to other countries. This is recognized by the institutions concerned—the Agency for International Development (A.I.D.), the U.S. Department of Agriculture, and the land-grant colleges and universities. In July 1964 these organizations held a joint conference to explore ways in which they could work together more effectively in providing technical assistance for rural development programs overseas.

Participation of the Department of Agriculture and the universities in foreign-aid activities has been going on almost from the beginning. As of March 31, 1964, 119 universities were carrying out projects in cooperation with A.I.D. under 252 different contracts. Many individual specialists in the Department of Agriculture and in the universities perform short- and long-term assignments for A.I.D. while on leave from their regular posts, and of course these institutions provide the reservoir of talent and skill in agricultural development from which A.I.D. draws permanent personnel.

So this is not a new program. It is an effort to improve upon present arrangements, with the objective of mobilizing the country's capabilities in rural development more fully. Foreign aid is a major instrument of the nation's foreign policy. Economic development in the poverty areas of the world is a major national enterprise. International rural development, therefore, must become a major concern to our domestic institutions which have the knowledge and experience in this field.

There are those who raise objections to a fuller employment of American agricultural institutions and technical experts in behalf of developing foreign agriculture. These objections fall into two general categories: (1) that such activity builds up competitors of American farmers in world markets and thus is potentially injurious to their economic welfare; and (2) that the United States cannot spare its agricultural scientists and technologists because they are needed at home to continue the process of farm improvement here.

Fears of foreign agricultural competition cannot be justified by experience or by realistic appraisal of the needs for food in the developing countries. Rural development cannot be realistically considered in isolation. It is part of general economic expansion and helps to stimulate a rise in production and income throughout the country. Invariably such a rise is accompanied by expanding imports as well as exports. For many years to come advances in farm production in the

[194]

poor countries will bring greater imports of farm products. As purchasing power in these countries increases, it means bigger export markets for the United States, including bigger export markets for agriculture.

As agricultural development proceeds, there will be shifts in export trade as the result of changing efficiencies and specialization. Some American farmers may find it advisable to change to other crops as markets change. It would be a mistake to allow the adjustments which might be necessary in a few crops as the result of foreign agricultural development to blind us to the total effect of greater purchasing power in the underdeveloped world.

Can America "spare" some of its scientific-technological experts now working on domestic agricultural problems for work overseas? The implication of this question is that when United States agronomists, animal nutritionists, or agricultural engineers work on foreign development problems, the result is a net loss of knowledge to American agriculture. This is not true. Technical knowledge learned in Iran and India becomes part of the fund of knowledge available to American farmers.

Here again one must examine the issue from all its sides. If it were a question of sharply reducing the effort for improving United States farm productivity in order to expand that effort in other lands, then the issue would be a matter of priority in the national interest. However, that dilemma does not confront us. United States agricultural productivity is advancing at a very rapid rate, with a momentum that is being maintained by commercial and private research. The country can well spare more of its public employees in agriculture for such a compelling national enterprise as the foreign development program without sacrificing progress at home.

In a major war, we quickly allocate manpower to the high-priority jobs. Perhaps we ought to look upon the A.I.D. program in somewhat the same way when it comes to skilled manpower requirements. It may be necessary, as time goes on, for United States agricultural institutions to increase their output of qualified technical personnel to fill

The abundance of modern agriculture is also reflected at the market level. Today's consumer is confronted with a wide selection of food—fresh, frozen, canned, and packaged—which she can either cook herself or buy to "heat and serve." By contrast, the old-fashioned country store carried

needs both at home and abroad. The supply of such experts is not necessarily fixed.

The public understanding of the issues here, and indeed of the whole aim and purpose of foreign aid, could be helped by a closer involvement of our educational institutions in the program. The benefits to the university community from more direct contacts with the outside world are obvious. The universities are a national resource which ought to be drawn upon for the contribution they can make to the

a limited stock. The proprietor, a carry-over from the old days, minds his store as if the industrial revolution hadn't happened. In addition to selling groceries, he serves as the local constable, barber, and cobbler.

nation's overseas development program. They can contribute by involving themselves in technical assistance and education for recipient countries—and by explaining the foreign-aid program to their own communities back home.

The benefits are not all one way. We gain from the building of free and stable societies; we also gain from the aid relationship or communication process, through enrichment of our universities, through greater participation in the world intellectual community.

A turning point in the conduct of foreign aid has been reached. The public institutions which generated the revolution in American agriculture are now turning their energies more intensively to rural development abroad.

The federal-state system of agricultural research and education is admirably adapted to serve the national need for overseas development. It is almost as though an unseen destiny guided us in the perfection of a method and a machine for stimulating world economic progress. There are no great departures from tradition or principle in this new effort. There is only a redirection to meet the demands of the new age.

Science and education know no national boundaries. The extension of American agricultural knowledge around the world is not a giving, not a handout process. Our fund of knowledge is not depleted by foreign technical assistance and education—on the contrary, it is enlarged.

Enlisting the land-grant universities and U.S. Department of Agriculture in the work of international rural development brings far more than technical know-how to bear on the problem. These agencies have learned from their rich experience how to create public understanding necessary to the process of social change.

Rural change cannot be ordered from above, even in totalitarian regimes, as the Communist countries have demonstrated. It must be desired by the people. It must be pulled by incentives. It must be powered by understanding.

A steel mill may be built and operated without the support or even the knowledge of the people at large. A disease-control program, such as spraying for mosquitoes to wipe out malaria, may be accomplished despite ignorance of most of the population about the procedure. But farming cannot be made more productive unless millions of farm people comprehend the things to be done and the reasons why.

The arts of conveying information and of persuasion and leadership are of the substance of rural development. And it is in this field of knowledge that America's federal-state extension system has so much to offer the underdeveloped countries.

Rural development is the heart of political democracy and individual responsibility. It is the greatest task of our times. Only the best efforts of many agencies from many advanced countries can start the underdeveloped countries toward self-sustaining growth.

We cannot afford not to do all of which we are capable.

BIBLIOGRAPHY

ACKERMAN, JOSEPH, and HARRIS, MARSHALL D., eds., *Family Farm Policy*. Chicago: University of Chicago Press, 1947.

BAKER, GLADYS L., et al., *Century of Service: The First One Hundred Years of the United States Department of Agriculture*. Washington: U.S. Department of Agriculture, 1963.

BENEDICT, MURRAY R., *Farm Policies of the United States, 1790-1950*. New York: Twentieth Century Fund, 1953.

————, *Can We Solve the Farm Problem?* New York: Twentieth Century Fund, 1955.

BENEDICT, MURRAY R., AND STINE, O. C., *The Agricultural Commodity Programs*. New York: Twentieth Century Fund, 1956.

BLACK, JOHN D., *Agricultural Reform in the United States*. New York: McGraw-Hill Book Co., 1929.

COCHRANE, WILLARD W., *Farm Prices: Myth and Reality*. Minneapolis: University of Minnesota Press, 1958.

HARDIN, CHARLES M., *The Politics of Agriculture*. Glencoe, Ill.: The Free Press, 1952.

HATHAWAY, DALE, *Government and Agriculture*. New York: The Macmillan Co., 1963.

HEADY, EARL O., *Agricultural Policy Under Economic Development*. Ames: Iowa State University Press, 1962.

JOHNSON, D. GALE, *Forward Prices for Agriculture*. Chicago: University of Chicago Press, 1947.

JOHNSTONE, PAUL H.; EVERETT E. EDWARDS, et al., *An Historical Survey of American Agriculture*. Washington: U.S. Department of Agriculture. 1940.

ROSS, EARLE D., *Iowa Agriculture: An Historical Survey*. Des Moines: The State Historical Society of Iowa, 1951.

SCHULTZ, THEODORE W., *Agriculture in an Unstable Economy*. New York: McGraw-Hill Book Co., 1946.

————, *Production and Welfare of Agriculture*. New York: The Macmillan Co., 1949.

————, *Economic Organization of Agriculture*. New York: McGraw-Hill Co., 1953.

————, *Transforming Traditional Agriculture*. New Haven: Yale University Press, 1964.

SHEPHERD, GEOFFREY S., *Farm Policy: New Directions*. Ames: Iowa State University Press, 1964.

SOTH, LAUREN, *Farm Trouble*. Princeton: Princeton University Press, 1957.

WILCOX, WALTER W., *The Farmer in the Second World War*. Ames: Iowa State University Press, 1947.

————, *Social Responsibility in Farm Leadership*. New York: Harper and Brothers, 1956.

Members of the Staff of Iowa State College of Agriculture and Mechanic Arts, *A Century of Farming in Iowa, 1846-1946*. Ames: Iowa State University Press, 1946.

Reports of Conferences of the Center for Agricultural and Economic Adjustment. Ames: Iowa State University Press. *Problems and Policies of American Agriculture*, 1959. *Goals and Values in Agricultural Policy*, 1961. *Labor Mobility and Population in Agriculture*, 1961. *Food: One Tool in International Economic Development*, 1962. *Farm Goals in Conflict*, 1963.

U.S. Department of Agriculture, *After a Hundred Years—The Yearbook of Agriculture*, Washington: U.S. Department of Agriculture, 1962.

70
71
72
74
75
76
77
79
81
83
85
88